ROCKHOUND GUIDE

Hoffman's

ROCKHOUND GUIDE

Includes:
How To Pan For Gold

Charles and Margaret Hoffman
Bert Webber, M.L.S., Editor and Indexer

A complete How-To-Do-It Guide on equipment, grit, polish and steps on

Gold Panning
Rock Hunting
Tumbling Gems
Gem Identification
Jewelry Making

With Special Section on Oregon "Rock" Museums

WEBB RESEARCH GROUP PUBLISHERS

Please address all inquiries to the Publisher:

WEBB RESEARCH GROUP PUBLISHERS
P. O. Box 314
Medford, Oregon 97501

Some of the content in this book appeared in the l970 and l973 editions of *Rockhound guide to rock hunting, gold panning, tumbling gems, gem identification, jewelry making* privately published by Charles and Margaret Hoffman and in the 1991 and 1993 editions published by Webb Research Group Publishers. It is the intent of the publisher to continue to recognize the expertise of the Hoffmans in this 1997 book.

The chapter on Gold Panning is adapted from that chapter in
Gold Mining in Oregon
which see in book list on page ii and in bibliography.

Cover Photograph by Bert Webber. A roadside scene in Central Oregon along Highway 26 near John Day Fossil Beds National Monument.

Library of Congress Cataloging in Publication Data:

Hoffman, Charles, 1907-1992
    [Rockhound guide to rock hunting, gold panning, tumbling gems, gem identification, jewelry making]
Hoffman's rockhound guide; includes: how to pan for gold ; Charles and Margaret Hoffman ; Bert Webber, editor and indexer.
    p.   cm.
Includes bibliographical references and index.
ISBN 0-936738-00-6
1. Precious stones—Collectors and collecting. 2. Grinding and polishing. 3. Jewelry making. I. Hoffman, Margaret. 1907– . II. Webber, Bert. III.   Title.
QE392.H64 1997   97-
553.8 – dc20   CIP

PREFACE

This book is a general guide for all rockhounds and gem fanciers regardless of their expertise, or lack of it, or where they live or normally vacation to go "rockhounding."

While several states are noted for large areas where precious and semi-precious stones can be found, Oregon is unique. This is due to the fact that nearly the entire state holds rich deposits. Accordingly, this book has highlights unique to Oregon and, Oregon is a gold panner's paradise.

Whether one likes to look for rocks roaming the hills and deserts or by strolling on the beaches, interesting gem stones can be found that are surprising in the beauty that is brought out when the material is polished.

An uncomplicated and inexpensive way to polish agate and other gem material is in a rock tumbler. This book will help one recognize gem stones and will provide specific information about how to operate a tumbler, how to make attractive gifts from baroques and to recognize the types of places to hunt for gem material.

When we started tumbling our own baroques, other lapid-arists practically worked behind locked doors and would say nothing about methods or equipment. Many pounds of grit and polish were used before we began to learn how to tumble rocks.

If readers already tumbles gem stones, we invite them to add our experiences to their knowledge. If one has never tumbled gem material, you can save the costs of this book with your first run. Rock polishers and saws and the next step if one chooses to go on but we believe the best way to get started is with the least investment in a tumbler.

Interest in hunting gold has never lagged. For those who wish to try their luck with gold panning, information is included on how and where to collect "samples" any how to pan them out. There is a thrill in finding one's own nuggets of which there are uncountable numbers yet to be found. Have at it!

Special Thanks

We appreciate and gratefully acknowledge the support of Pansy D. Kraus, Graduate Gemologist, F.G.A., for reviewing the manuscript and offering valuable recommendations.

The interest and encouragement of Robert L. Hill, Sr., Graduate Gemologist and Curator, Crater Rock Museum, Roxy Ann Gem & Mineral Club, Inc., Central Point, Oregon is appreciated. The Club is the sponsor of a major, annual, rock and gem show in Medford, Oregon in early spring.

Photographs provided by the late Charles S. Hoffman
unless otherwise noted.

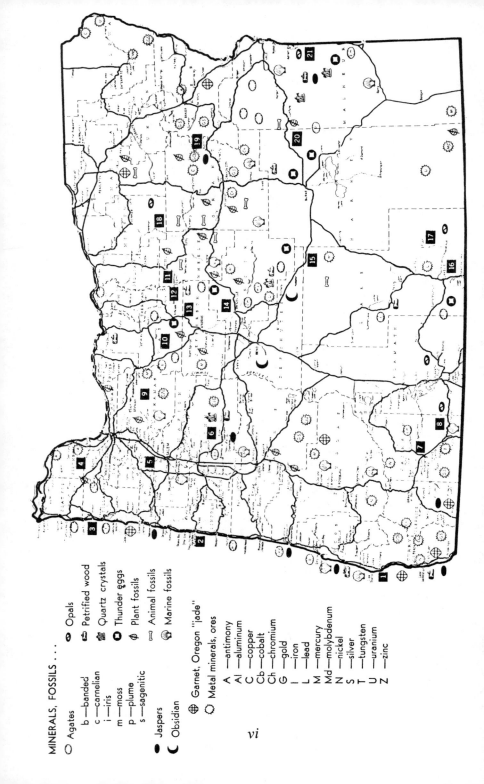

MINERALS, FOSSILS . . .

Agates
- b—banded
- c—carnelian
- i—iris
- m—moss
- p—plume
- s—sagenitic

Jaspers

Obsidian

Opals

Petrified wood

Quartz crystals

Thunder eggs

Plant fossils

Animal fossils

Marine fossils

Garnet, Oregon "jade"

Metal minerals, ores
- A —antimony
- Al —aluminum
- C —copper
- Cb —cobalt
- Ch —chromium
- G —gold
- I —iron
- L —lead
- M —mercury
- Md —molybdenum
- N —nickel
- S —silver
- T —tungsten
- U —uranium
- Z —zinc

vi

Minerals and Fossils – Oregon Statewide – Where to Look

[1] SOUTHERN OREGON BEACHES – Gem quality agate, jasper, petrified wood, serpentine, Oregon "jade" (*grossularite garnet*). On Merchant's and Whiskey Run beaches find agatized myrtle, etc., blue and white banded agates, flower jaspers. "jade" and serpentine in gravel bars of Rogue and Illinois Rivers. Eocene marine fossils at Cape Arago State Pk. Pliocene-Pleistocene fossils in cliffs south of Cape Blanco Lighthouse. [2] CENTRAL OREGON BEACHES – Agate, jasper, Oregon "jade," petrified wood; good tumbling material from Lincoln City to Newport, sagenitic agates with needle-like inclusions, bloodstones, on beaches between Yachats and Heceta Head, espec. near mouths of Big, China, Cummings, Tenmile and Squaw Cks. Miocene marine fossils, shells, bones of whales, etc., at Beverly Beach State Pk. [3] NORTHERN OREGON BEACHES – Jaspers, agates, petrified wood, Oregon "jade." Near Oceanside are jaspers, sagenitic agates, large specimens on Tillamook County beaches. [4] CLEAR CREEK – In gravel bars of creek bed; Carnelian plume agates, jaspers. [5] WILLAMETTE RIVER – Gem quality agates from river bars and gravel company dredgings n. of Salem to s. of Corvallis; agates in metropolitan Portland. [6] SWEET HOME – Petrified wood, banded agate, carnelian agate, jasper, crystal-lined geodes, silicified fossil wood with grain and ring structure. Look in Ames Ck. Calapooya Riv. s. of town. In fields, woods, streams, banded agates, crystal-lines geodes, fire-engine red jasper. Large carnelians at Chandler Mt. Holly purple or Calapooya blue agates near Holley. [-7-] MEDFORD – Moss and dendritic agate, jaspers, milky chalcedony in Agate Desert area of White City to Eagle Point. [8] GREEN SPGS MT. (about 9 mi e.. of Ashland) – Banded blue-grey agate, crystal-lines geodes, fossil shells of Cretaceous marine life. [9] CLACKAMAS RIVER – Cinnabar, petrified wood, jaspers. In riv. above Estacada has gem quality cinnabar, petrified woods, dark green bloodstone. [10] SUNFLOWER FLATS – Banded agate, crystal-lined geodes, jaspers on Wapinitia cut-off sw. of Bear Spg Forest camp. Bring shovel. [11] CLARNO – Fossil nuts, leaves and prehistoric mammals, blue eagle nodules, petrified wood, jaspers, zeolites, barite crystals. Famous Clarno Fossil Beds east of John Day Riv. Mammal Beds reserved for scientific exploration. [12] ANTELOPE – Moss agate, jasp-agate, massive botryoidal agate, geodes, agatized woods. <u>Antelope area is one of the best known sources for gem-grade agates in Oregon.</u> Large moss agate in shades of red, blue, green, yellow in ck e. of town; agatized wood 4 mi e. of town on hill to right of road. *Obtain permission before entering private land.* [13] PRIDAY RANCH (commercial) – Thunder eggs with blue agate, plume agate, green, red, moss agate, opals, polkadot. Area is about 15 mi. e. of Madras on Hwy 97 turn right on old Hwy 97 go 2 mi to jct of rd to Ashwood which follow about 9 mi. Attendants will show where diggings are located. Pay per-lb. fee for gem material. [14] PRINEVILLE – Thunder eggs plume, carnelian, moss agate, nodules, petrified wood. At Eagle Rock area e. of town find outstanding red and black plume agate. In Maury Mts, beyond Eagle Rk find green, red, brown, golden moss gate, white plume agate both "float" and "in place." South of town Bear ck area has red and green moss agate, nodules and agatized wood. Wildcat Mtn area ne. of town has Morrisonite, a hard jasper-like similar to "wonderstone of Utah in thunder eggs. [15] GLASS BUTTES (between Bend and Burns on Hwy 20) — Obsidian in black, variegated and silver sheen volcanic glass near mile post 79 on s. side of hwy. Continue e. for red and gold sheen obsidian in great quantities toward mile post 81, going s. toward cinnabar mine then 2 to 3 mi on right fork of road. Watch for rainbow and double-flow obsidians. [16] LAKEVIEW – Thunder eggs, agate, jasper, nodules, agatized wood. Bullard and Deadman Canyon e. of town blue and purple agate, agatized wood, jasp-agate, orbicular jasper. Nr. Hwy 95 is blue agate from 2 to 5 mi s. of city. In Crane Ck. area s. of town find agate-filled thunder eggs. At Kelly Ck, agate, jasper, thunder eggs. Search vast Dry Ck. area w. of town: agates. [17] HART MOUNTAINS – Agate nodules, fire opal, crystals, sunstones, jasp-agate resembling Morrisonite. Sunstone on desert flats w. of mtns. nodules and jasp-agate in mtn canyons. Fire opal on high peaks of w. rim. [18] OPAL BUTTE – About 35 mi s. of Heppner on Hwy 207 and on forest roads opal-filled nodules. [19] GREENHORN – Fossils, varieties of gem matter, frags of fossil Cretaceous fern "trunks" (*Temoskya*) may be uncovered about 1 mi ne. of Greenhorn (ghost town) n. of Austin. Best spots e. of abandoned IXL mine toward Olive Ck. Easily identified fossils usually golden color, some red. Greenhorn fern is jasper-hard and takes good polish. Look in ck beds and gold dredge trailings down riv. from Bates to Susanville. Bring shovel. [20] WARM SPRINGS RESERVOIR – Black dendritic and white plume agate found along w. shore 18 mi s. of Hwy 20 at mile post 171 when water is low (Aug. into winter). Fossils of Pliocene plants in road cut on Hwy 20 about 8 mi w. of Juntura. Pliocene animal fossils on n. side of hwy w. of Drinkwater Pass. [21] SUCCOR CREEK – Thunder eggs, jaspers, petrified wood s. of Adrain along ck to Rockville. Thunder eggs contain Pastelite or agate with inclusions of black dendrites, green moss or golden plume at good site 19 mi s. of Adrian where road and ck converge.

—Data from *Oregon Rocks, Fossils, Minerals.* Oregon Dept. of Transportation n.d.

vii

ROCKHOUND RULES

Oregon is a collector's paradise, but even in a paradise it is wise to follow a few simple rules . . . certainly they will tend to assure the best possible success.

1. Select several sites within a fairly small area to avoid spreading valuable collecting time too thin . . . become informed on the material available and its exact location.

2. Don't hesitate to ask local collectors for information about selected sites . . . check with rockhound clubs wherever they are found.

3. Bring along the proper tools and equipment—including boots and sturdy clothing—for field work . . . depending on the material sought, you may find use for a rockhammer, shovel, prybar, sledge and chisel, or light pick mattock.

4. Make special preparations for seasonal weather conditions—canteens, caps and sunglasses for the desert, warm jackets for the mountains, etc.

5. Obtain permission of land owners before entering private property . . . don't leave campsite debris scattered about and BE CAREFUL WITH FIRE.

6. Take care in entering abandoned mine shafts—you enter at your own risk.

7. Don't throw rocks from cliffs and endanger persons who might be below . . . use proper care in handling tools.

8. Take only the material you will use and leave the rest for other collectors.

Contents

1. Tumblers

Tumblers of various sizes and shapes can be purchased from lapidary shops. Price ranges from $10 for small tumblers holding three pounds of agate to larger and much more expensive models. The 6 lb. or the 12 lb. tumblers will fill the needs of most rockhounds. The larger tumblers will hold more but they also require the running of a much larger load which may not always be desired.

The most efficient shape of tumbler barrel is hexagon or octagon. The most efficient length of the barrel has been found by experience to be less than twice the diameter. There are arguments in favor of the barrel with the length less than the diameter. The 6 lb. tumblers on the market have this narrow shape. They impart a lot of tumbling action.

The flat sections in the sides of the hexagonal and octagonal barrels lift the stones higher before the tumbling action starts, thereby increasing the grinding or polishing action per revolution. In the round barrel there is more slippage of the load against the side so that the gems tumble a shorter distance than they will in a hexagonal barrel of equal diameter.

In a round barrel of our own design we installed two fins to act as lifters in order to facilitate the tumbling action. We removed them after finding that they caused the gems to be lifted and dropped, causing breakage. A liner will give much better results.

Rubber tires can be used. Disadvantages are the difficulty of cleaning out the tire casings, and of protection against unwanted dirt and grit during the polish run. This can be avoided if an inner tube is also used. Also, there could be one tire for rough grind, one tire for fine grind, and one for polish. This would reduce the amount of cleaning required.

If you decide to build a tire tumbler, it can be hung on a spindle, from which the tire gets its turning power. Or, it can be set in a frame and rested on two rollers, one of which has power applied from a 1/4 H.P. motor. For rollers, 5/8" cold rolled iron can be used and covered with 5/8" I.D. heater hose. We have made rollers this way, and also by using the two wringer rollers from an old washing machine. The antique business is making these hard to find.

The power can be applied to either roller (push, or to pull) but the pulling action probably operates with less slip. Any passenger car sized tire will do.

Some rockhounds use an inner tube inside of the casing, and place the stones in the tube. A 4" or 5" slit is made longways to the tube on the outside (exposed) surface of the tube. The gem material is loaded and emptied thru this cut. The opening is sealed by making two rubber faced blocks of wood and fixing two carriage bolts in the block which goes on the inside of the tube. The bolt ends should extend toward the exposed side of the tube. The block going on the outside must have holes drilled to match the bolts. Wing nuts are put onto the bolts and tightened. Each block should be covered with rubber held in place by waterproof cement. The surfaces of the rubber covering should be moistened with water before sealing. This makes a more watertight fitting.

This type tumbler will hold 25 to 30 lbs. of gem materials. Use 3 lbs. of grit for rounded water worn agate, and 4 lbs. of grit for rough materials, with approximately one gallon of water.

After the rock, grit and water are placed in the tube, and the tube closed, pump a small amount of air pressure into the tube so as to help it hold its shape in the open tire casing. The presence or absence of tread on the tire does not matter, but there should be no large, open breaks in the casing.

Long before open tumblers were on the market, we designed and used several. Eighteen inch steel pipe with a bottom welded to it was used. The barrel was approximately 18" long and rested on rollers held in a frame at a 45° angle. A bumper at the bottom had a movable core which was kept greased. The bumper was centered, holding the barrel in position and permitting it to turn. Power was applied to one roller. The rollers were made of 5/8" cold rolled iron covered with 5/8" heater hose.

The tumbler held about 25 lbs. of gem material. It had no problem of gas pressure, as did some of the enclosed round barrels we previously made. The open tumbler did a fairly good job of tumbling but it was noisy. The cost was greater than for a tumbler of similar size sold in rock shops at retail. Also, the heavy steel barrel was difficult to handle during cleaning.

The covered, round barrels made of sheet steel and welded were also noisy and wore out after one year of use. We replaced these with commercially made, lined tumblers which show no wear after many years of continuous use.

We have built several types and sizes of tumblers, keeping complete cost records and found that the cost exceeded the retail price of comparable sizes of tumblers on the market. The person who already has motors, bearings, and a welding outfit can save on the costs. Otherwise, buying a ready-made tumbler is less expensive.

A word of caution is in order. Do not clean tumbler barrels in the sink. The material will harden into a mixture closely resembling concrete and will clog the plumbing. Clean the barrels in the back yard or where the residue can do no harm. About 20% of the material being tumbled will be worn off during the rough grind and about 5% during the fine grind.

We have found but very few rubber or neoprene lined barrels that require opening during operation to relieve gas pressure. The amount of gas generated is affected apparently by (1) the type of liner material, (2) the type of material being tumbled, (3) whether or not a retardent such as sal soda is used, and (4) upon outside temperature. When you have built a tumbler or purchased one, check it frequently for gas pressure until you find out whether or not that particular barrel generates gas under the conditions used.

Unlined steel barrels and glass jars definitely require opening periodically to let the gas escape unless they have a valve or pet-cock vent which can be opened to relieve the pressure. During warm summer weather the barrel may need to be opened every two or three days. During cooler winter weather the barrel may not need to be opened as often.

The gas generated in the barrel is partially dependent upon the material being tumbled. Petrified wood seems to generate the most gas, which is apparently marsh gas, such as methane. The gas is flammable. It also has an unpleasant odor.

It appears to be the same gas that is formed in marshy ponds where stagnant water and decaying wood will form bubbles of gas on the surface of the water. If you hold a lighted match near one of these bubbles and break the bubble, the escaping gas will ignite.

Petrified wood which still shows grain and texture still has some of the original cellulose. In fact, years ago some of the chemists at the University of Wisconsin recovered a small amount of cellulose from petrified wood and made paper out of it.

We have held a lighted match near the top of a newly opened tumbler barrel holding petrified wood and found that the gas will burn. This experiment is not recommended.

Ordinary gem stones such as agate and jasper do not generate very much gas during tumbling but caution must be observed when using unlined, closed barrels. We have heard of unlined steel barrels bursting from the pressure and of the same thing happening with small tumblers using quart jars.

In addition to the gas, another source of pressure is the use of a detergent such as Tide. This can be used both during the grinding and during the polish runs. The Tide aids the tumbling action for both grinding and polishing. This pressure can be decreased by including a pinch of sal soda with the load.

If a homemade round tumbler barrel is being used for polishing, it can be improved by lining it with thick leather. A water-proof cement such as a gasket cement must be used. Put the smooth side of the leather against the metal, so the stones will be against the rough texture of the leather. After each polish run, the lining should be checked to see if the cement is holding. Any rough bits or chips that may have worked into the lining should be removed. After being lined for polishing, this barrel must not be used for grinding, because all of the grit can not be cleaned out of it for subsequent use in polishing. Extra barrels may be obtained for most of the tumblers on the market, permitting the use of one barrel for polishing only.

The gas produced by the grinding action in unlined, steel barrels can be considerably reduced by the addition of up to 1/2 teaspoon full of sal soda or of baking soda. The sal soda seems to act as a better water softener, but it reacts with some of the types of liners being used. It has been found that the use of Tide without baking soda or sal soda can create acetylene gas, which is explosive. So precautions should be taken against the presence of open flame or cigarettes near tumbler barrels which are being opened.

Use capacitor type motors on your tumblers and do not run them continuously without having them plugged into an "overload" switch. The electric shop or hardware store can provide you with this type switch for the size of motor being used. If a bearing starts to grab, or a power drop causes the motor to overheat, the overload switch will turn off the electricity to the tumbler. This almost eliminates the chance of fire or other trouble that might arise when an unattended motor is left running.

The outlet in the equipment room at our shop has switches of this type between the power outlet and the tumbler motors. We have had up to six tumblers running night and day and never shut off except for repairs. Even when we are out of town for several days we let them run. A few times we have found them shut off when we returned. A flick of the overload switch started them turning again.

One reason for keeping the tumbler running is the fact that the grit and sludge in the barrel will harden or "set". Turning the barrel again on the tumbler may not release the material, which may have to be dug out with a long-handled screwdriver.

We have heard of many types of tumblers, some floating in the ocean while anchored by cable, some have been fixed to water wheels in small streams. In eastern Oregon we have seen them hooked up to windmills for power. We have watched tumblers made of Mason jars, quart cans, 5 gal. buckets, tires, cement mixers and 2x4's.

There is no limit to the ingenuity of a rockhound.

2. Operation

Optimum tumbling speed depends upon the size and type of barrel being used, the type of material being tumbled, and whether it is being ground or being polished. Many of the manufactured types of tumblers can not be speeded up or slowed down to adapt to specific needs. They have included pulley sizes which give the average speed required for most operations.

Where possible, step pulleys of equal size should be installed on the motor shaft and on the shaft turning the barrel. When the step pulleys are in opposite positions, the belt can be moved from one pulley step to another to increase or to decrease the speed of the barrel.

Fig. 1.   Use of Step Pulleys

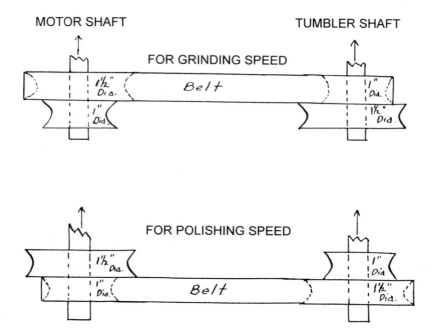

The pulley diameters shown in Fig. 1 are not the sizes necessarily needed on a tumbler, but are shown only as examples of the use of step pulleys. Tumbling speed is reduced by decreasing the pulley size on the motor shaft, so that the motor will turn more times in relation to the tumbler, thereby slowing the barrel speed.

A larger pulley diameter on the motor will increase the tumbler speed. In nearly every case, the polish operation will be improved and with less breakage when the tumbler is revolving at a slower speed than ordinarily used for grinding. One exception to this is in the case of a load of extra large stones, such as 2½" to 3½" sizes in a 12 lb. tumbler. Less breaking will occur in tumbling large material this size when it is ground and also polished at a slow speed.

If the tumbler is not adaptable to installation of two step pulleys, the normal speed can be slowed for polishing by reducing the size of the pulley on the motor shaft. This will require a longer belt, or the motor can be moved on the base and a new set of holes drilled in the motor platform. If the speed of the barrel cannot be reduced, the effect of the existing speed can be reduced by the use of additives and cushioning agents referred to in a following section.

Most of the 12 lb. capacity tumbler barrels are approximately 9½" in diameter and revolve at about 22 revolutions per minute. For these a polishing speed of approximately 18 RPM would be about right.

The speed can be too slow for good sliding action, so you may have to experiment with a particular size and shape barrel. With a 9½" diameter barrel, the circumference is approximately 29½". An RPM of 18 represents a surface speed at the circumference of about 44' per minute. From this, the optimum speed for various size barrels can be calculated.

Tire tumblers operate efficiently at somewhat higher speeds because of the cushioning effect of the tire. A surface speed per minute of 60 sfpm (surface feet per minute) at the outside circumference of the tire is about right.

The following formula can be used in changing pulleys if you wish to alter the speed of a tumbler:

$$D = \textbf{Diameter of pulley on tumbler shaft}$$
$$S = \textbf{Speed shaft must turn}$$
$$SM = \textbf{Speed of motor}$$

$$\frac{D \times S}{SM} = \textbf{Diameter of pulley on motor}$$

Example, with a 12 lb. capacity tumbler:

On this tumbler, as with most hobby sized tumblers, the power from the motor goes via belt to a large diameter pulley which is attached to the end of one of the two shafts on which the barrel rests.

The diameter of these rubber covered shafts is approximately 1". Pi times diameter equals circumference. So multiply 1" x 3.1416 and the circumference of the shaft is found to be about 3-1/8". The barrel has a diameter of 9-3/8" and therefore a circumference of 29½". For the barrel to turn at 22 revolutions per minute, the circumference of the barrel must travel 649" (i.e. 29½" x 22 RPM). Divided by 12", this represents a rate of 54 surface feet per minute. The 1" shaft turning the barrel must therefore revolve at a rate of 216 RPM to turn the barrel 22 RPM. This is arrived at by dividing the 649" by 3-1/8".

With a 10" pully (i.e. wheel) on the shaft which turns the barrel, we use this formula to determine what pulley size should be on the motor shaft to arrive at the speed of 22 RPM for the barrel.

D (Dia. of pulley on tumbler shaft) = **10"**
S (Speed which the shaft must turn) = **216 RPM**
SM (Speed of Motor) = **1750 RPM**

$$\frac{10" \times 216\ RPM}{1750} = ?\ \text{(Dia. of pulley on motor shaft)}$$

$$\frac{2160}{1750} = ?$$

or, 2160 ÷ 1750 = 1¼", dia. of pulley on motor shaft.

This would be normal grinding speed. If a slower speed was desired for polishing, such as a barrel speed of 18 RPM for example, the formula would show what diameter pulley should be put on the motor shaft. First, calculate the surface speed per minute at the circumference of the barrel turning at 18 RPM:

18 RPM x 29½" Circum. = 531" surface speed per min.

531" ÷ 3.125" Circum. of 1" shaft = 170 RPM which the 1" shaft must turn.

$$\frac{10" \times 170\ RPM}{1750} = ?\ \text{(Dia. of pulley on motor shaft)}$$

$$\frac{1700}{1750} = ?\ \text{(Dia. of pulley on motor shaft)}$$

or, 1700 ÷ 1750 = 1" Dia. of pulley on motor shaft. (To nearest size).

16

Most ¼ HP motors turn at either 1750 or 1800 RPM. The speed is shown on the metal plate fastened to the outside of the motor. The formula shown here will be useful in the event you wish to change the speed of a tumbler you have bought, or to determine speed and pulley sizes on a tumbler you are building.

The best speed for the grinding action allows the stones to slide over each other (Fig. 2, Example A). Speed which is too fast will throw the stones and cause fracturing (Example B). Speed which is too slow will permit the stones to slide against the side of the tumbler, developing flat sides on the layer of stones against the side of the barrel (Example C). In addition, the tumbling action will be almost nil.

Each grinding run should start with the barrel from ⅔ to ¾ full of material. We recommend that the water level be just under the top layer of stones. Too much water seems to decrease the grinding action (Fig. 3).

The first rough grind in 60/90 silicon carbide grit or in #120 grit will take off approximately 15% to 20% by weight of the gem materials. The load should then be cleaned and sorted. Part of the load will be ready for a finer grind, but a part will usually need another rough grinding. We have boxes of stones in different stages, sorted out until a tumbler load is ready.

A similar sorting should be done after completion of the find grind. The fine grind will wear off not more than 5% by weight. Rough spots and broken edges will not be smoothed by the fine grind during a week's run. So do not get in a hurry and place the stones in the fine grind hoping they will smooth out, for in 9 cases out of 10 they won't. Any rough edges should be re-ground in #60/90 or #120.

The reasons for sorting are obvious. Some stones are ready for the next step after one run and there is no need to grind them further. Also, added grinding might be undesirable. For example, in rough grinding fire agate the areas of the fire should be exposed but should not be ground away. In beach agates, we prefer to keep some of the white layers which are common to many of the smaller stones. Too much rough grinding will grind away all of this layer. With desert roses and snake agate, the rough grind should smooth them but not grind away all the shape.

Sorting is also recommended for size and type of material. Amethyst, Apache Tears, and rose quartz (to name a few) need special treatment. Agates placed in a run of amethyst or rose quartz will usually cause breakage. Apache Tears will be "sugared" on the ends if placed in an agate mix. The agate is not only harder and will scratch obsidian, but it is heavier and damages the Apache Tears when they hit against each other. Incidentally, obsidian can be run with Apache Tears. Both materials are the same composition and cause no problems. Amethyst should be run alone, as should rose quartz and rutile quartz.

Fig. 2.   Barrel Speed

Example A

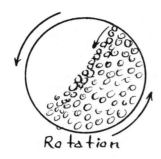

Rotation

Correct Speed

Top layer slides
down, layer after
layer.

Example B

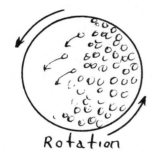

Rotation

Rotation Too Fast

Top stones are
thrown to far
side and to bottom.

Example C

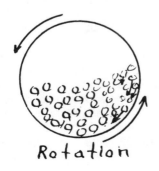

Rotation

Rotation Too Slow

Slippage against
side, without being
raised high enough to
tumble.

Fig. 3. Load Levels

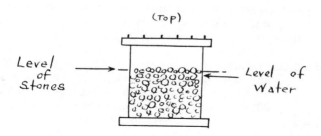

(TOP)

Level of Stones →

Level of Water ←

Sorting for size must be done to prevent placing a large proportion of big stones in a run. One or two large stones may be found to tumble satisfactorily while a half dozen large stones might break up the rest of the load.

The need of mixing slabs with smaller rounded stones is mentioned elsewhere. The size of the large stones and the proportion that can be successfully tumbled increases somewhat with the larger barrels.

The small size shoe box from a men's clothing store will easily hold a load for a 12 lb. capacity barrel. Keep a note on a slip of paper in each box showing which grit or polish run it is being collected for. Then whenever a box contains a full load for any particular stage it can be started. A full ⅔ or ¾ of a barrel is needed in going from a #60/90 run to a #220 run, or from a #220 run to a polish run. At each step, there must be a full load for best results. A barrel ⅓ full or even half full will not grind well or polish well.

The length of time required to complete a rough grind, a fine grind, or a polish run is approximately one week of continuous operation. By that time the cup and a half of rough grit, or fine grit for the 12 lb. load will be used up. In weight, this is equal to a generous pound of grit for 12 lbs. of gem material.

If a polish run is not completed in a week, they may need sorting to wash out grit and to remove broken pieces. We usually check a polish run by lifting the lid and taking out three or four stones of different sizes. Wash them in hot water so they will dry quickly then hold them under a strong light to see if they have a bright shine. Even when a load is all one kind of material, a few broken pieces can roughen up the entire load and prevent a good polish.

Whatever the shape, size, or source of power of a tumbler, the tumbling action of grinding and subsequent polishing is brought about by causing

19

the stones in the barrel, or tire, etc. to slide down the incline of stones without damage. These stones are again carried to the top and again slide to the bottom in a continuous action.

We have used demonstration tumblers with glass lids which permit a look at the inside of the tumbler while it is revolving with a load. This gives a graphic picture of what goes on inside the tumbler.

The round barrel has the greatest length of slide for the diameter of the barrel but it also has more slippage against the smooth side. Tumbling efficiency is increased when a hexagonal shape is used which decreases the distance of slide in relation to diameter of the barrel, but it increases the sliding action by raising the stones to a higher level before they start their downward slide. In order to reduce breakage to a minimum, a hexagonal barrel can be turned at a slightly slower speed per minute than for a round barrel of the same diameter without loss of tumbling efficiency.

To insure the optimum length of "slide", the barrel must be filled ⅔ or ¾ full. Loads of more than this proportion "clog" the barrel and permit only a small part of the load to slide a very short distance (Fig. 4).

Fig. 4. Clogged Barrel Due to Overloading

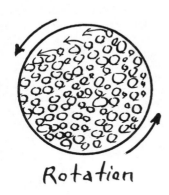

Little or no tumbling movement.

Rotation

It is suggested that you frequently listen to the sound your tumbler is making. A new load that makes a swishing sound is just right, both for grind and for polish. If you have a load that is loudly "clicking", the stones are in danger of breaking. If it is a new run just started, it needs more cushion, fewer large stones, more small stones, or a combination of all three. This assumes that the primary trouble isn't one of running the barrel too fast.

The clicking is another way of telling when the rough grit is used up. When a proper charge is started on rough grind it will swish with only slight clicking. The grit seems to cushion the stones. When the grit is used up, the clicks become louder. This is the time to change the load.

For one who is just beginning tumbling, here is the basic procedure for the average tumbler with a 12 lb. capacity barrel:

Step 1. Rough Grind

1. Fill the tumbler barrel approximately ⅔ or ¾ full of agate or other material with the largest size not over about 2" across. If you are going to run Apache Tears then the entire load must be Apache Tears or a combination of tears and obsidian. If you are running slabs, then do not fill the entire load with slabs but mix small stones with the slabs. Slices of gem material have a tendency to stick together when being tumbled, and this can be decreased by including other shapes and sizes in the load.

2. Add water until the water level is slightly below the top level of the gem stones.

3. Pour into the barrel 1 ¼ cups of #60/90, or #100, or #120 silicon carbide grit. Add a pinch of Tide and a pinch of sal soda or baking soda.

4. Wet the top liner of the barrel and wet the neoprene gasket before fitting the gasket over the studs (bolts) sticking up from the barrel. Put on the metal lid and screw down the wing nuts, using finger pressure only.

5. Place the barrel on the tumbler and run for approximately 7 days continuously. If you have to turn it off at night or part of the day, then the number of days run must be increased accordingly. At the end of this time, the grit should be used up. Hammer broken materials will probably take another run with rough grind. Water worn material such as beach agate will finish more rapidly. If you can feel grit in the barrel at the end of the 7 days, then close the barrel and continue running for a few more days.

Step 2. Fine Grind

1. Pour the contents of the barrel into a wire screen so that the stones may be washed, and also wash the inside of the barrel. Place the stones in a container such as a plastic bucket (because it will not mark the stones) and rinse them with hot water. Spread out the stones on a cloth or towel and sort out into separate boxes the stones that need to go back into a rough grind and the ones that are ready for the fine grind. If you do not have enough stones ready for fine grind that will fill the barrel at least ⅔ full then you will have to place the stones needing more #60/90 back into the barrel and add enough new material to make up a load that fills the barrel

⅔ full. When you have about 12 lbs. of gem material ready for the #220 grind, place them in the tumbler barrel.

2. Add enough water to come just below the level of the stones.

3. Put in 1¼ cups of #220 grit and a pinch of Tide and a pinch of sal soda.

4. Wet the top of the barrel liner and also the rubber disc and place it over the bolts. Place the metal cover over the bolts and tighten the wing nuts finger tight. There is one type barrel on the market which does not use bolts and wing nuts, but has a neoprene lined metal lid that snaps into a groove in top of the lining.

5. Run approximately 7 days continuously. If grit can be felt in the barrel when it is opened at the end of 7 days, then close it and continue running it for another day or so.

Step 3. Polish

1. Pour the contents of the barrel over a screen out in the yard, or over a container where the sludge can be caught and disposed of without putting it down the plumbing. Wash the stones and the barrel thoroughly. Any rough or broken stones should be sorted out and kept for the next #60/90 grit rough grind.

2. Add approximately ½ cup of Tin Oxide polish powder and ½ cup of Tide with just enough water to make a soupy mixture. If you are using other polish in place of Tin Oxide, more polish will be needed. Silica powder will require a full cup, and the mixture should be thinner than when Tin Oxide is used. If Titanium Dioxide is used, put in about ¾ cup of the polish and about one pint of water.

3. A protective cushion should be added, such as a double handful of vermiculite, clean scraps of leather, hard wood blocks, or similar material. Vermiculite will soak up water, so if it is used, another ½ cup of water should be added to the mix. The vermiculite is an exploded mica and can be obtained at lumber yards or nurseries where plants are sold. It is used for insulation and also for compost.

4. Run the polish load approximately 7 days. At the end of that period open the tumbler barrel and check the polish. If the baroques are not shiny, then tumble them a few more days.

5. At the end of the run, pour the contents over the screen and wash the stones and the barrel with warm water.

To summarize, on each step the barrel must be from ⅔ to ¾ full to obtain the best tumbling action. The rough grind is the most important step for if the stones are not ground smooth they will not look attractive even when polished. The fine grind will not wear down broken or rough spots. If one week on #60/90 grit does not smooth some of the stones, sort these out and save them for another rough grind.

Except for broken stones, all material run with the fine grit will be ready for the polish run. Obsidian and Apache Tears must be run without mixing with other types of material. Also, these will need an additional grind, with real fine grit such as 4-F or #600 grit. They also require more "cushion" when tumbling. The best we have found for this is vermiculite. This protective agent will wear down and must be replaced every few days when running Apache Tears. The load will not need emptying and cleaning, just open the lid and drop in another handful of vermiculite.

With Tin Oxide polish, less polish may be used if it is replaced with Tide. We have successfully used ¼ cup of Tin Oxide and ¾ cup of Tide for the polish run for a 12 lb. load. This polish should be quite thick, so be sparing with the water.

Lapco polish and silica need to be run as a thinner solution. You will constantly improve your polishing techniques by experimenting with different mixtures. Keep a record so as to gain from your own experience with different mixes and materials.

Remember to oil the nylon bearings with a drop of oil about once a month.

If the tumbler being used is smaller or larger than a 12 lb. capacity, the proportions of grit, water, and polish should be changed accordingly. A barrel with a 24 lb. capacity would require 2½ to 3 cups of grit, one full cup of polish, etc. One of the small quart-can tumblers will hold about four pounds of rock so the amount of grit would be cut to ⅓ lb. and the polish cut to a third of a cup of silica.

It should be mentioned that tumbler barrels referred to as a "12 lb. size" will hold different amounts, by weight, of different materials. The weight of a load will also vary according to the size of the material being tumbled. Because obsidian is lighter than agate, a barrel ⅔ full of obsidian will weigh less than will a barrel ⅔ full of agate, rhodonite, or jade.

A 12 lb. capacity barrel ⅔ full of hammer broken agate will hold about 9 lbs. However, the same barrel ⅔ full of agate ready for the polish run will hold a 12 lb. load.

The amount of grit will therefore vary somewhat for each load, depending upon what type and size of material is being tumbled. Even though the 12 lb. capacity barrel may have only 9 lbs. of rough, broken agate in it, you should use a full pound or pound and a quarter of grit for more grinding will be necessary than for a load of smoothed, water-worn beach agate.

The maximum sized stone that can be tumbled will be smaller in a quart size tumbler than in a 12 lb. capacity tumbler, and the maximum size for a 12 lb. capacity tumbler will be smaller than the maximum size for a 24 lb. tumbler. The quart cans will not efficiently tumble stones much larger than 1" in diameter, or slabs of about the same size. The 12 lb. barrel will take a few stones in each load of approximately 2½" size.

A barrel with a 40 lb. capacity will take a dozen or so stones of 4" to 5" size.

For a 6 lb. tumbler, the grit and polish needed will be approximately half of the amount required for a tumbler having a 12 lb. capacity. In other words, for the rough grind with #60/90 grit, use about ½ cup of grit. For the fine grind with #220 and finer grit, use about ½ cup. Use about ½ cup of polish for the polish run.

For the small tumbler having a capacity of 3 lbs. of agate, cut these amounts to ¼ cup.

Remember to keep the nylon bearings oiled about once per week. If the motor on the tumbler has an oil hole for lubricating, it will require oiling no more often than once per month. If the motor is sealed, with no oil hole, it is the type that requires no added lubrication.

In every case where a few large stones are included, be sure to include small stones for cushioning and leave out such items as thin slabs, or quartz crystals or similar materials that are easily fractured. A few pieces of hard wood about the size of the stones being tumbled will also help.

Keep a record of what is in each tumbler barrel, even if you have only one barrel. Over each barrel at our shop, we have a spring clip hanging on a nail. The clip holds a piece of paper showing the barrel number (numbered on each lid), the date of the last grit or polish change then in progress, and a brief reference to the kind of material in the load, such as "Beach Agate", "Petrified Myrtlewood", Slabs & Misc.", etc.

A record like this will save a lot of arguments with yourself as to what you put in the barrel and when you did it.

3. Abrasives

The sizes of grit used is partly a matter of personal choice and partly dependent upon the type of material being tumbled. A coarse grind using #60/90 silicon carbide grit, followed by a fine grind using #220 & Finer grit will prepare most gem stones for the polish run.

The rough grind is the step that does most of the work, for only the coarse grit will grind out the holes, chips and major imperfections.

The #220 and Finer grind will smooth the surfaces of the stones in readiness for the polish.

When we refer to #220 grit, we mean the grit which is classed as "#220 & Finer". In other words, the grit grades from #220 as the largest size, down to some fines. Some rockhounds object to this and will use only grit which is classed as "#220 Graded", which means it is all #220 in size and has no fines in it. This graded grit is considerably more expensive and for most tumbling needs the less expensive #220 & Finer is perfectly satisfactory.

Likewise, some rockhounds prefer to use #100 grit or #120 graded grit for the coarse grind. For most tumbling operations we recommend the #60/90 because it is less expensive and does a good job.

We have tried coarser grit such as 30/60 but do not recommend it. Even after most of the grit has worn out during a run, there will be large grains remaining. These will keep putting heavy scratches on the gem material.

After the #220 & Finer grind, soft stones such as Apache Tears and sunstones need a third grind, using a #320, or a 4-F, or even a #600 grit. With each grit, the amount used is roughly one pound per 12 lbs. of gem material.

If you do not have scales for weighing the grit, use a full cup measure of grit per load in the 12 lb. capacity tumbler. At the end of 7 to 9 days this amount of grit will be used up.

After washing the stones with the hose, rinse them in a plastic bucket filled with hot water then gently pour the bucket full of stones back into the screened box where they will quickly dry.

The use of a plastic screen and a plastic bucket is desirable because iron or aluminum screens and buckets will mark the polished stones. The screened frame as described on Page 28 will conveniently hold the load from a 12 lb. tumbler. For a larger tumbler you will need a proportionately larger screened box.

Fig. 5.   12 Pound Loads of
Rough and of Polished Baroques

There are three general types of material that can be tumbled: (1) baroques, (2) slabs, from pieces that have been cut with a diamond saw, and (3) preforms.

Baroques tumbled from water worn material such as beach agates will lose about 15% by weight during the rough grind and about 5% during the fine grind. Baroques tumbled from hammer broken material will lose about 20% by weight during the rough grind and not more than 5% during the fine grind.

The size of a load for a 12 lb. capacity barrel before and after tumbling are shown in Fig. 5. The largest of these pieces are about 1½" across.

If there is a noticeable amount of unused grit in the tumbler when the stones are removed at the end of a run, then either too much grit was used or the run was not long enough.

Rough material such as hammer broken agate and jasper will require more grit than will water worn material such as beach agates. Rough material will also require longer running time than the minimum of 7 days.

As an unusual example, we tumbled a load of synthetic corundum and spinel for over twelve months. This material is so much harder than agate that months and months of grinding with #60/90 grit were required, with grit changes approximately each week.

One effect of the use of grit more coarse than #60/90 is to roughen and pit the surface of the gem stones, particularly on slabs. This condition can also result if too much #60/90 grit is used or if too little water is used during the rough grind. If a roughened surface develops, the #220 grind may not smooth out the material and a re-run on #60/90 will be needed with the correct proportions of grit and water.

In each barrel, the material should fill the tumbler at least ⅔ full but not more than ¾ full. Water should be added to about an inch below the top level of the gem material to be run. If vermiculite is used, add more water to compensate for the amount soaked up by the vermiculite.

In any abrasive run regardless of grit size, we have found that the best results are obtained when all the grit in the tumbler has been used up. For instance, with #60/90 grit, the individual grains become smaller and smaller as they carry out their grinding action. This is true also of #220, or 4-F grit. Therefore, at each step the grit becomes finer and the smoothing action becomes more pronounced when all the grit in the tumbler has been worn completely out.

If you have used a lap wheel, you will have found that a similar condition occurs. If you are spreading #120 grit on the wheel it is best not to go to the #220 grit for the next step until all of the #120 grit on the lap wheel has been worn down by the rock being lapped. If this is not done, the surface of the gem material will have deeper scratches than it would otherwise have and which the #220 grit will not remove without much time and effort.

When a tumbler is opened for inspection of a coarse grind run and it is found that more grinding is needed, do not just throw in more grit and resume tumbling. The "goop" in the barrel will become so thick that the grinding action is greatly retarded. When a thick "goop" develops in the barrel the stones seem to become "etched" with rough surfaces.

If grit is still present in the barrel, which can be quickly determined by sliding a finger tip over the inside surface of the barrel, then close it up and continue tumbling for a few more days. However, if the solution is a thick goop then it should be cleaned out. If the grit appears to be gone and the stones are still obviously rough, then wash the load and the barrel and re-charge with water and grit and resume tumbling.

The best method we have found for washing the stones after a run is to build a wooden frame about 12" x 20" out of 1x4 boards and nail plastic screen onto the bottom edges of the 1x4's. Then add another frame of 1x4's on the edges where the screen is nailed. This keeps the stones from getting into the grass or dirt.

On top of the plastic screen nailed onto the frame, we place a loose piece of plastic screen of fine mesh. The tumbler load is then dumped into this "box" and the contents washed with a hose until all the "goop" is gone. Do not do this in the sink or laundry trays. It will plug them.

Slabs should be mixed with baroque materials for best results. The nubbins should be ground off or broken off prior to tumbling. They do not seem to disappear during tumbling. The nubbins are the small rough spots left when the diamond saw is completing the cut. They can detract from the appearance of an otherwise attractive slab.

Fractures which may break and separate during the tumbling process should be broken before starting the rough grind. They can be broken with a hammer or snapped apart by using a pair of nippers or pliers.

Slabs of uneven shape can be raised in quality by first breaking them along fracture lines, and then breaking them further as needed for the size and shape desired. We try to break as many as possible of the same approximate size and shape so that pairs can be found for earrings, with similar shape, size and color for matching pendants. (Fig. 6)

28

Fig. 6. Slabs of Agate Before and after Tumbling

The large round slab of Brazil agate shown in Fig. 6 is 4" in diameter. Only one slice this large should be included in a 12 lb. barrel load at one time. And no large, heavy pieces of rough material should be included in the load with a slab this large.

When a trim saw is available, long pieces of rough agate can be sliced for tumbling, with matching pairs available after tumbling. Agate filled limb casts are fine for this because many slices of the same shape and size can be cut from a limb cast three or four inches long.

The thickness of each slice should be nearly the same as possible, for two pieces that would otherwise match for earrings do not look pleasing if one slice is thick and the other is thin.

Slabs will lose about 20% by weight in the grinding. They are more attractive when the saw nubbins are broken off or ground off, and should be rough ground long enough to smooth the edges of the slabs.

Preforms would lose their shape if they were rough ground as much as rough agate. The length of time in the rough grind will depend upon the material. Goldstone crosses, for example, will grind away twice as rapidly as would an agate cross.

Do not include any large or heavy stones with the preforms, and use plenty of cushioning agent. There are many possibilities in the tumbling of preforms. Just use reasonable care to protect them. Cut the rough preforms larger than the finished size which is desired, to compensate for the 20% loss which occurs during tumbling.

Obsidian (Eastern Oregon)
—Photo by Bert Webber

4. Grinding Additives

There is a constant search for materials which will increase the speed of grinding away pits and smoothing rough surfaces on the gem materials.

The following brief list indicates some of the factors for and against some of these agents:

RICE HULLS.

One of the best. Use about one pint of rice hulls in a 12 lb. capacity barrel. The hulls pick up the grit and carry it over the surfaces of the material being tumbled. If it is to be used in a polish run, be sure it is grit free.

PIECES OF SILICON CARBIDE GRINDING WHEELS.

Very good. You can buy the pieces of broken grinding wheels. If not available, use the small cores left on your (and your friend's) grinding wheels and break them into pieces about the size of the material being tumbled.

Don't put pieces of #100 wheels or #120 wheels in a #220 run. The pieces of wheels do a real fine job of working down rough material such as hammer broken agate and jasper.

The only bad feature is the difficulty of finding and sorting out all of the small bits and pieces when you want to change the load to a finer grit. If you used the wheel chunks in a #220 run and put this load into a polish run without sorting out all of the wheel bits, the polish will be less than bright. These wheel bits develop baroque shapes and can look remarkably like some of the baroques you hope to polish.

WET SANDING CLOTH.

We keep a box on the work bench near the drum and disc sanders. Every time we trim a wet sanding belt for the drum, we toss the scrap pieces into the box. Likewise, discarded belts are cut into small 1" or 2" squares and later used in the grinding stages of tumbling.

The belts must be cut into small pieces for if this is not done, the large pieces will curl while in the tumbler and it seems they always curl with the grit side on the inside of the curl.

HARDWOOD BLOCKS.

Small pieces of hardwoods have been used with considerable success, especially to cushion larger stones. Cut pieces about 1" in length from ½" dowel rods. Use a handful to each 12 lbs. of rock. Any hardwood will do, but the pieces should be smaller than the size of the stones being tumbled.

The pieces used for polish should not be mixed with the pieces used for grinding, nor should grit sizes be mixed. Keep the blocks sorted when not in use.

BALL BEARINGS.

Poor, but soft metal such as lead or brass would be better than steel.

We have tried all sizes of steel bearings up to 1", using only one size per load as well as using mixed sizes. The larger, heavy ball bearings seem to crush the grit and reduce the grinding action. They belong in ball mills for crushing ore, but not in tumblers.

Lead B-B shot are much better than the other metals. The lead seems to pick up the grit and carry it into the rough places in the material being ground.

SAL SODA.

Sal Soda greatly increases the sliding action in the tumbler, as well as decreasing the formation of gas. It likewise decreases the foaming of Tide. We use approximately a teaspoonful in a 12 lb. load.

The sal soda acts as a "wetting agent", cutting the sluggishness of the sludge formed by the material being ground away from the baroques.

The sliding action required in tumbling is greatly increased. When we started using neoprene lined barrels we had to greatly reduce the amount of sal soda used for it seemed to soften the liners. A pinch or two can be used in a 12 lb. lined barrel with no ill effects but it is something to watch, then act accordingly.

BAKING SODA.

Similar action as with sal soda, but not quite as effective.

"BITS".

We use a 1" steel plate with wooden side-boards as an anvil for breaking stones. Many times the quality of a baroque or slab can be upgraded by breaking the stone along a fracture or breaking out a flaw.

Stones too large for the tumbler can also be broken into usable shapes and sizes. The result is an accumulation of tiny slivers and pieces of gem materials which we call "bits".

For a rough grind we throw in about a cup full of bits to 12 lbs. of gem material. These bits seem to do as much good as any grinding agent we have tried. They eventually become polished by moving them up through each stage of tumbling. We sack them and find many uses for their kaleidoscope of colors, not only for cement-on jewelry but in mosaics, fish aquariums, jewelry boxes, and plastic items.

5. Polishes

There are several polish powders which work effectively in tumblers after the gem material has been properly ground. If the stones are not smoothed, none of the polishes will make them shine.

There are some stones of course which will not polish with a bright, shining surface. Soft material such as sandstone, some rhyolites, sugar quartz and other porous stones will not polish.

If you have no rockhound friend who can sort your material for the first run or two, the next best is to learn by experience. The learning period can be considerably shortened by use of one general rule. If the rough material has no shine, even on a broken surface, then it probably will not take a good polish.

This rule is noticeable on jasper. Some of it is shiny and hard and polishes beautifully. Some of it is dull and lifeless appearing and does not polish well. So at least part of the success in getting a good polish is in selecting gem stones that will polish and learning to reject those that are not capable of being polished. The latter kind are known as "Leaverite". In other words "leave 'er right where you find it"!

Before starting each polish run you should thoroughly wash the barrel and the gem material. We have heard of some rockhounds who add fine grit such as #600 to the polish powder and run it for a longer period of time.

We do not recommend the above procedure for it seems much more reasonable to separate each step, for the polish can not start its final polishing action until all of the #600 grit is worn out, and by that time some of the polish is also worn out.

The individual who combines the #600 grit with the polish and gets a good polish, would probably get an even better polish by finishing the #600 grit run, washing the stones and then starting the polish run.

A polish is not something put onto the stones, but is something taken off, and the things taken off are scratches.

Each grit, pre-polish, or polish removes scratches left by the preceding agent until the point is reached where the scratches remaining by the last step are too small to be seen by the naked eye. This final result is a bright polish.

In addition to grit which can hurt a polish run, rough and broken pieces also can scratch the other stones in the tumbler. For this reason always sort out any stones with broken edges before starting the polish run. Also sort out and hand wash any stones (such as Texas Biscuits) which have holes in quartz pockets which can hold grit.

Polish powders can be purchased in the bulk or can be obtained in sets made up together with packages of grit needed for each step.

The following polish powders are the principal ones used in tumbling and available in the bulk. Our experience with each polish is summarized:

POLISH	COST	EFFECTIVENESS
Alundum	Inexpensive	Useful as a prepolish, before using a final polish.
Silica	Inexpensive	Good. Creates a bright polish, but the need to run as a very thin solution allows considerable breakage if large material is run. Use of a cushion material sometimes thickens the polish mix to the point where it will not create a bright polish.
Rouge	Moderate	Fair. Very messy to use and requires considerable washing to remove the polish from the stones.
Cerium Oxide, OP	Expensive	Good. With hand polishing on a felt wheel, cerium in optical grade is hard to beat but in a tumbler it is not as good as Tin Oxide. Be sure to use optical grade. The lower grade can cause scratches which may be due to the inclusion of hard crystals or foreign matter.
Radiant	Moderate	This is a trade name. It is a very good polish but is difficult to find on the market.
Levitigated Alumina	Moderate	Good. This polish is also known as "white rouge".
Air Float Tripoli	Moderate	Good.

Tin Oxide, CP	Very Exp.

Very good. Until recent years this polish was cheaper than cerium but now it is much more expensive. It is the best polish we have found for use in a tumbler. The "CP" is for "Chemically Pure". It costs more than the cheaper grade but is worth the difference.

Tin Oxide gives its best polish when used as a thick solution. This also cushions the stones. There is less breakage than with many other polishes and a very bright polish results.

It can be diluted with a detergent such as Tide, which cuts the cost without detracting from the exceptionally bright polish.

In a 12 lb. load, use ½ cup of Tin Oxide, or mix with Tide up to ¾ cup and decrease the amount of Tin Oxide to ¼ cup. These are dry measures.

Josephinite (iron)
Josephine Creek,
South Central Oregon
—Photo by Bert Webber

Cushion material such as vermiculite can be added without detracting from the polish. This is a necessity with fragile material such as Apache Tears and sunstones.

Linde Ruby Powder	Expensive

A good polish, which can be used alone or in combination with Tin Oxide.

Titanium Dioxide	Moderate

This polish is almost as good as Tin Oxide and is about half the price. Tide can be used to thicken the solution and decrease the amount of Titanium needed.

Aloxite Buffing Powder A-1 fine	Expensive

Very good. Also, try on softer stones such as turquoise which is normally hard to polish.

35

| Tide | Inexpensive | This powder is used in combination with many polishes and is also used as a final polish to further burnish the polished baroques. Gem material that has gone through the polish run can usually be made even brighter by a day or two in a thick Tide solution. |

The comments on these powders and polishes are solely the personal opinion of the authors. You might experiment with each one and reach different conclusions. The reference to cost, for example, is only relative for in the case of a polish which is shown to be "expensive", the need to use less of it than other polishes may make it actually inexpensive.

Where several drums are available, such as with a 3-drum tumbler, it is suggested that one barrel be used exclusively for polishing. It will remain free of grit and will do a better job of polishing.

We can not agree with the advice of some operators that the polish solution can be drained and used again. We have saved the solution and used it again. The benefit derived from re-use is debatable.

Each time the polish solution was re-used it was necessary to keep adding new powder in order to obtain a good polish. The additional polish powder needed was almost as much as was required to start a new polish run so we can not see that anything was gained by starting with the old polish solution. It seems that the polish wears out, just as grit wears out.

A benefit that does result from re-use (with the "bits" strained out and new polish added) is the cushion effect of the thicker solution. However, any sharp bits of broken material must be screened out of the polish, for its presence in the polish run can prevent a good polish from developing. Broken or rough edges will scratch the other stones.

The belief that polish wears out can be checked on hand work. In polishing cabs, a slightly brighter polish can be obtained when the stone is buffed vigorously for several moments after the final bit of polish is used on the wheel or applied to the cab. In other words, you should not add polish powder to the tumbler a few hours before emptying the load nor should you add grit to the tumbler a few hours before stopping a grit run.

There will be times when your ingenuity will be taxed in developing a fine polish. We recall a run of sunstones well ground and smoothed beautifully but they would not shine.

They still looked "foggy". We finally tried a trick previously used with Apache Tears. In that case, we could not get a real fine polish until we added a handful of previously polished tears to the batch. They then took on a bright polish.

So we added a handful of brightly polished sunstones from a previous run, and all the sunstones took on a beautiful polish within two days. It is somewhat like placing an artificial egg under the hen.

The tumbler can be used for preparing materials other than gem stones. Abalone shells make baroques of pink, blue, and green that are beautiful in jewelry or in plastic table tops. The shells can be hammer broken or can be sawed with a diamond saw or even with an ordinary hacksaw. If sawed "dry" as with a hacksaw, do not inhale the dust. It is mildly toxic. We discovered this while hand carving Tiki charms from pieces of abalone shell.

Tumble the shells in fine quartz sand, such as is used in sand blasting equipment. The sand can be obtained from industrial supply firms. Use enough water to just cover the load and tumble for two or three days. Wash and dry as you would baroques, then replace the shells in the tumbler and use ¼ lb. of tripoli polish for a load in the 12 lb. capacity barrel. Run this for two days, then clean out, wash and dry the shells and tumbler.

The last step is to fill the barrel half full of hardwood sawdust, rice hulls, or other cushion material and add ¼ lb. of tin oxide, silica or other polish powder. No water is used. Run this dry mixture for several hours and the shells will take on a nice polish.

This last polish procedure can also be used by hunters who hand load their own shells. If the re-used shell casings need polishing or burnishing, make up a dry load of sawdust and shell casings with ¼ lb. of polish powder and run the load a day or so. The casings should not be tumbled with grit in a wet mixture, because it would be almost impossible to get the grit and sludge out of the bottom of each shell.

For you bottle hunters, collect the broken pieces of the bottles that have those beautiful colors. Break them into usable sizes and tumble them. They come out prettier than much of the glass "slag" that is sold for tumbling.

Glass must be tumbled alone, without mixing it with agate or other type of material.

Precious coral can be tumbled, but skip the coarse grit and start with #220 or even #320 grit. Check the load frequently to determine whether or not the material is grinding properly without loss of an undue amount of coral. Finish with a good grade polish. It is better to tumble the coral only enough to eliminate the rough ends and edges.

When hand polishing gem stones on a felt wheel, a brighter polish can frequently be achieved by adding a pinch of oxalic acid crystals to the "slurry" of tin oxide, cerium oxide or other polish being used.

The same crystals also help the polish run in a tumbler. To a 12 lb. capacity tumbler barrel, add one or two tablespoons full of oxalic acid crystals to the polish. The stones will come out a little bit brighter when these crystals are added.

Spear points found buried at a spring east of Glass Butte, Lake County at camp-site of Stephen Meek's Lost Wagon Train of 1845. (lower) Transluscent obsidian spear point. Note: Specimens obtained in 1974 five years before the Antiquities Act (October 1979) that prohibits digging for arrow heads. Details of this field trip are in *The Search For Oregon's Lost Blue Bucket Mine* by Charles S. Hoffman. —Photo by Bert Webber

6. Cushion Material

Many types of materials have been used as "cushion" material for the dual purpose of (1) increasing the grinding or polishing action, and (2) decreasing the fracturing and breakage while being tumbled.

We have tried all that we have heard of, plus a few more ... Some good, some bad!

SUGAR.
Addition of sugar to the water in the tumbler makes a sticky mess with no appreciable benefit.

HONEY.
Ditto. It is best on biscuits.

SAWDUST.
Fair. Most of the sawdust available to us has been from softwood. Sawdust from hardwood is noticeably better.

RICE HULLS.
Good for rough grinding and was used for polish as well until we found that the hulls were not clean, but were gritty. It may be that we had a poor grade of rice hulls.

If the hulls are left in the rough grind or fine grind for a full week (a double handful for a 12 lb. barrel) they will mostly disintegrate. However, if put into the tumbler only a few days before opening, they are still in matty fibers which are difficult to completely wash out of the batch of stones you are cleaning for the next step.

RUBBER.
Good. There is a difference in types of rubber. The kind used on heels which mark your floors will also mark your gem stones. Good quality rubber such as used in rubber gloves if fine.

CORN STARCH.
Good.

NEOPRENE.
Excellent.

PLASTIC PELLETS.
Fair. They do a fair job, but are a real nuisance in cleaning up the stones and the barrel. They become imbedded with grit, so do not use them in a grit run then use them later in a polish run.

WOOD BLOCKS.

Hardwood blocks, smaller than the size of the stones being tumbled are very good. Use a large handful in a 12 lb. load. Do not use the same blocks in a polish run that were previously used in a grit run.

LEATHER SCRAPS.

Good. Cut into small pieces.

WOOL SCRAPS.

Good. Cut wool cloth into small squares and use in polish run of Apache Tears.

SANDING BELT SCRAPS.

Good for grit runs. Cut into small pieces to reduce curling.

CELLULOSE WALLPAPER PASTE.

Fair. Add one tablespoonful to a 12 lb. capacity barrel.

VERMICULITE.

Excellent. This material is one of the best cushion agents we have found. However, if the vermiculite has grit or sand in it, do not use it with polish.

It is made of "exploded" mica and is used for compost and also insulation.

Vermiculite is one of the "secrets" of our success in tumbling Apache Tears. One word of caution, however. The tumbler must be opened every few days and vermiculite added. It wears out from the tumbling action. In a 12 lb. capacity barrel we use a double handful of vermiculite. About a half cup more water must be added to compensate for the amount soaked up by the vermiulite.

— — —

You may find other cushioning agents that work better for you than do any of these. It will be a case of trial and error. Use of a cushion is always needed during grinding of some materials such as Apache Tears.

During all the polish runs, a slower speed is desirable, but where this is not possible, the alternative is to use a cushioning agent. This will decrease the effect of the speed by preventing the gemstones from striking each other so hard.

Enough of the cushioning agent should be used so that any loud clicking noise is replaced by a "swishing" sound of the gem stones sliding over each other as the tumbler revolves.

7. Baroques Can Be Beautiful

The amateur rockhound can recover much of the cost of his lapidary supplies and equipment by making various types of gifts for friends and relatives.

Even so, there is no requirement that baroques be "practical". We know a couple who place all of their tumbled stones in a shallow basket on their coffee table. Their visitors admire the stones and the supply dwindles away as the baroques are given to people who admire them. Baroques are to be enjoyed.

Neither do we concede anything to the "purist" who sniffs and states that baroques are not lapidary work because their size and shape are accidental, so to speak. We wish to inform such purists that some of the most beautiful sunsets we have ever seen were formed by an accidental arrangement of clouds. Some of the most beautiful cabs we ever made were cut from slices that accidentally were sawed thru an attractive combination of lines and color.

Large polished slabs make attractive and interesting mobiles when they are capped or diamond drilled and hung with a piece of transparent nylon fishline. Hang one in the window where the sunlight can strike it. Each breath of air will mové it slightly, sending rays of color across the room. (Fig. 7)

Large tumbled slabs also make attractive bases on which to cement figurines of various types.

Tumbling of preforms is a very useful method of preparing gem material for jewelry purposes. Material which has been slabbed can be cut into preformed squares, diamonds, triangles, or rectangles. There are overhead swing saws that are adaptable to making cuts at the correct angles, slicing almost thru the slab, in both directions. The slab can then be broken off along the cuts. Vises are also on the market for holding slabs or for cutting of preforms.

If the polished pieces are to be used in cement-on jewelry such as for earrings, then the finished size in millimeters is not too critical. However, if the preforms are to be fit into a mounting with raised sides or bezel, then the finished size must be slightly smaller than the mounting.

To end up with 16/16 mm stone for a cuff link mounting, the stone prior to tumbling may have to be cut 17/17 mm. Soft material may have to be

41

Fig. 7. Hanging of Tumbled Agate Slabs

Fig. 8. Tumbled Preforms of Tiger-eye and Snowflake Obsidian

even larger to start with. The amount that is ground away in tumbling will depend upon the hardness of the material, thickness of the slab, and length of time in the rough grind. Material such as goldstone must be left in the rough grind a shorter time than for agate preforms.

When the nubbins left by sawing are ground off, very accurate preform shapes can be made in the tumbler. (Fig. 8)

Use of a tumbler to finish beads is not advised. We spent several hundred hours slicing jade, cutting it into strips, cutting the strips into cubes and then diamond drilling the cubes. The corners of each cube were then ground slightly in hope this would start them on their way to becoming spheres in the tumbler.

All seventy-two of them were put into a tumbler for the rough grind with small beach agates. The tumbler was checked frequently. Instead of developing into rounded beads, the cubes became more and more misshapened. The entire project turned out to be a lost cause. If beads are wanted, then a bead mill is the answer, not a tumbler.

We have successfully tumbled crosses made of agate and of goldstone. The results are very attractive. It is suggested though that preforms to be used for pendants should not be drilled prior to being tumbled. The stones tend to wear unevenly near the drilled hole, or may break out at the hole because it is weakened at this point. The preforms can be satisfactorily drilled after they are tumbled.

The quality of gem stones that will come out of a tumbler as polished baroques will be limited by the quality put into the tumbler. There are some rockhounds who look down on tumbled baroques. They may be the same ones who say that only poorer grade gem materials should be put into a tumbler. It is a certainty that if poor grade material is put into a tumbler, then poor grade material will come out of it.

Many gem stones such as dendrite agate from Agate Flat on Green Springs Mountain in Oregon, and fire agate from California and Arizona can be hand worked better after careful tumbling. Care must be taken in not grinding off too much material with the rough grit.

We have found that baroque style cabs of fire agate can be better worked up into rings and other jewelry after the gem has been tumbled. The areas of fire can be more easily located and the shape of the stone better developed to make the best use of fire in the gem stone.

With gem material such as chalcedony roses, a short time in rough grind, followed by fine grind and polish can result in beautiful baroques which can be used on pins or pendants with custom made mountings.

44

Garnets which are too small for faceting or cabochons can be tumbled to make beautiful gems. But do not put large, heavy pieces of material in with the garnet. The small, polished garnets are very adaptable for use in baroque cement-on jewelry.

Most rock shops have the "findings" used in making baroque jewelry. The medium sized stones as well as the tumbled slabs which are not to be handworked can be capped by cementing bell caps on them.

These caps can be purchased in either sterling or gold filled, but most are termed "yellow" or "white". Good quality caps will hold their color for years. The "white" metal of best grade is rhodium plated. This finish will not tarnish, and is even used as a finish on many sterling chains and mountings because sterling will tarnish unless it is continually burnished by wearing, such as in a ring. The "yellow" caps are usually covered by a thin gold wash, or by a finish called "Hamilton Gold" which actually has no gold in it.

Epoxy is the best cement we have found for securing the caps to the baroques. This cement is water-proof and if properly mixed and applied it cannot be pulled away from the stone. We have demonstrated this by using a pair of pliers in attempts to pull off bell caps. The metal will tear first. We have even pulled out a small section of gem material without pulling off the epoxy.

Epoxy is not recommended for attaching baroques to adjustable rings. The epoxy is so hard that in bending the ring to adjust for size, the bond is sometimes broken. A better cement for adjustable rings is a ceramic cement that remains flexible. One that we like to use is called "Glass and Ceramic Adhesive", by Dow Corning.

Several good brands of epoxy are available. The epoxy is mixed half and half and stirred with a toothpick for one minute. The epoxy and the hardner may come in small tubes or in squeeze bottles.

Use a smooth slab of clean agate or glass and pour out a small mound of epoxy then pour out an equal mound of hardener beside it. Do not put one on top of the other or the amounts cannot be compared for equal size after they have run together. When the two equal portions are mixed together thoroughly they turn white, but the epoxy will harden into a clear, transparent bond.

Before applying the epoxy, use a small piece of cotton or kleenex and wash the top of the stone, using a good grade lacquer thinner or acetone. The caps can be washed in a small container holding the thinner.

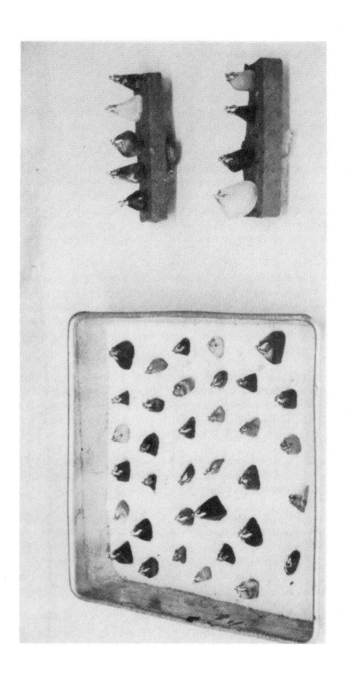

Fig. 9. Baroques Held in Salt and Clay, for Epoxy

After washing the surface of the stone, and of the metal to be cemented on, do not touch those parts with your fingers. If that is done, enough oil from the skin will be left on the stone to prevent a good bond. For the same reason, no cleaning agent with oil in it such as soap or alcohol can be used.

In most cases, it is easier to shape the prongs of the bell cap to fit the stone before applying the epoxy. Have a pan of salt on hand, or strips of modeling clay. (Fig. 9)

With a toothpick, place a small amount of epoxy on top of the gemstone and also on the inside of the bell cap. Push the cap down onto the stone and carefully set the stone upright in the salt or press it into the strip of clay. Be certain that the cap is right on top of the baroque or it may slide down.

Check the caps for about a half hour to see if they are straight. If they have moved out of place they can be straightened. After about a half hour the epoxy will "set" and no more movement will occur.

The epoxy will harden in about eight hours or can be speeded up by placing a heat lamp over them. We usually do not use heat before the epoxy has "set", otherwise the cement tends to get thin and run.

There are several designs of bell caps for different purposes and different sized stones. The principle designs are (1) 7 prong, (2) 2 prong, (3) 4 prong twist, (4) epoxy cup, and for slabs (5) leaf type which is bent together and cemented onto the front and back sides of the polished slab. The first three types are generally used for baroques. (Fig. 10)

Fig. 10. Types of Bell Caps

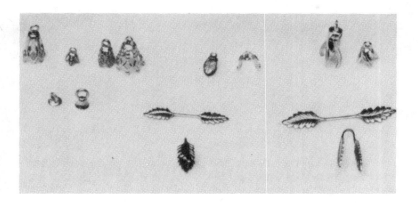

After the epoxy has set, the excess can be cut off with a knife blade and the thin areas which were spread by finger tips can be scrubbed off with lacquer thinner. If you wish to remove a bell cap or other stone that has been epoxyed, soak it in lacquer thinner in a closed bottle until it loosens. Do not soak it in an open container for the lacquer thinner will evaporate before the epoxy is dissolved.

Check the baroques that have been capped by inspecting the prongs of the caps for any ends that stick up away from the stone after the epoxy has hardened. Use a burnisher or the handle of a pocket knife and push the ends of the prong toward the gem stone. This makes a better appearing job and also prevents snagging of cloth on the tops of the prongs.

Capped stones have an almost endless variety of uses, including dangles for earrings, pendants, chain bracelets, key chains and for tips on bola cords. A jump ring is used to attach the bell cap to the bracelet or other mounting. In using jump rings, open the ring by using two pairs of thin nose pliers and twist the jump ring open. (Fig. 11)

Fig. 11.   Jump Rings Should Be Twisted Open and Shut

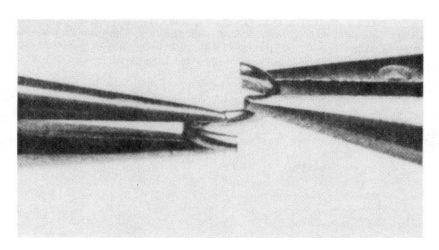

Attach the neck of the bell cap and the link of the bracelet or chain over the jump ring, then twist the jump ring to close it. Do not spread the jump ring apart or it will not close properly and the round shape will be lost. (Fig. 12)

48

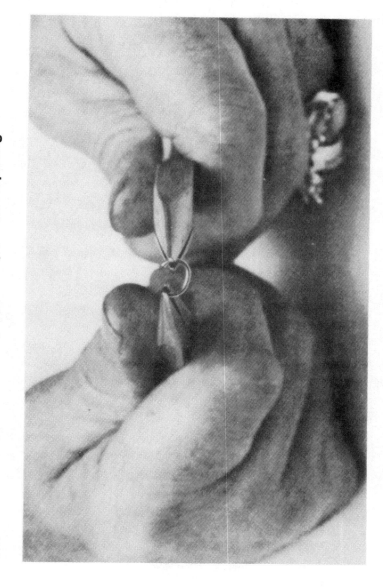

Fig. 12. The Way Not To Open A Jump Ring

There are many designs of bracelets, bola slides, earrings, pins, pendants, rings and other mountings that use baroques with a flat surface for cement-on jewelry. Some of the mountings do not even require a flat surface, but have a cupped design which will easily hold a small baroque. Several types are illustrated in Fig. 13.

Fig. 13.   Mounting for Cement-on Jewelry

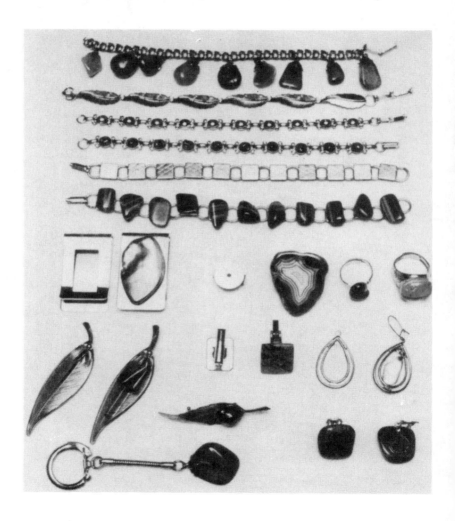

For cementing when a quick bond is required, Aron Alpha or a similar adhesive can be used. This material should be kept refrigerated or at least kept in a cool place. It is more expensive than epoxy and it will not fill up any spaces between the parts being bonded.

The big advantage is the quickness with which it sets. Another advantage is that no mixing is required.

Fig. 14. Baroque Mountings

The #201 is low in viscosity and quick in setting. The #202 is high in viscosity and slow in setting. But "slow" is a relative term. We used some of this in bonding epoxy type bell caps to small beach agates, holding them down with slight manual pressure. In most cases, the stone could not be adjusted after ten to twenty seconds.

The instructions issued with this adhesive should be followed. Avoid breathing the vapor, and avoid contact with the skin or eyes. Needless to say, keep it out of the reach of children. We use finger stalls, purchased at the drug store, to keep the adhesive from the fingers while cementing with Aron Alpha. Holding the bell cap with a pair of tweezers will help keep the adhesive from the fingers.

Soaking with acetate will usually dissolve the adhesive if you wish to remove the stone from a mounting.

Similar adhesives are on the market under several different trade names.

In addition to cement-on jewelry and dangle jewelry, baroques may be used in the ball type of mounting which may then be filled with glycerine and sealed. There is also a "bird cage" type with the spring of the metal holding the stone inside of the cage. There are also mountings with "ears" or prongs which can be bent down over the stone to hold it tightly. A few designs are formed like a "basket" to hold the stone by the spring of the metal (Fig. 14). New mountings are brought out practically every season, so keep checking with your favorite rock shops for the latest design.

The polished baroque bits make colorful frogs, turtles and other figures poured with plastic. Soft, pliable molds can be obtained for making these figures. Hold the turtles on a board but hold the frogs in an empty egg carton. Pour them half full of plastic and then drop in a half teaspoon of baroque bits. Stir them with a toothpick to get the plastic on all surfaces of the stones and to force the small stones into all corners of the mold. Add more stones and then pour plastic as needed to fill the mold even with the top (Fig. 15)

It is best to do the pouring where there is adequate ventilation. Plastic gloves should be worn to keep the plastic and hardener from the hands. Temperature makes a difference in the setting of the plastic, because a harder finish is achieved when the plastic is poured in a room temperature of at least 70 degrees. The figures will harden overnight. After being taken out of the molds, the figures should be heated slightly in an oven, or left in warm sunlight for a day or two.

Fig. 15. Pouring Plastic Figures

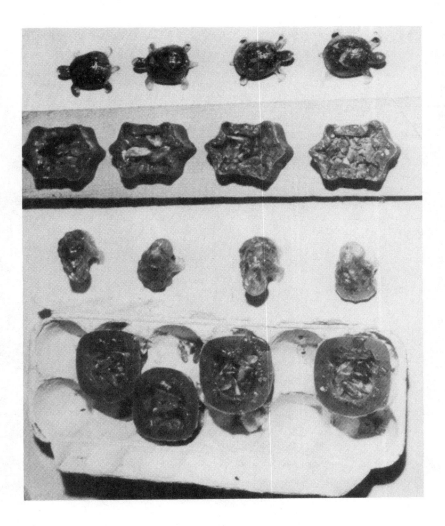

The larger polished baroques may be used in plastic table tops and the polished bits used as filler. Stones do not have to be polished for use in plastic but it seems to improve their color. Polished amethyst baroques in the frogs and turtles have a superior color to those in which the rough, unpolished pieces of amethyst were used. On gem stone such as tigereye it does not seem to make so much difference.

Polished baroques make attractive floors in fish aquariums. They can be used in fireplace fronts, in wall or floor tile, in outdoor fountains and flower gardens, in double layered coffee tables with lights underneath, in panels beside doors or on each side of a fireplace, in mosaic crafts and in as many other uses as the imagination and talent of the individual permits.

So start tumbling. Go for Baroque!

Rope agate flow called "Agate Wing." Found at Priday Ranch, North Central Oregon See map page 2. —Photo by Bert Webber

8. Identification of Gem Stones

This section is written for the beginning rockhound who wants to learn how to identify the rocks he picks up in order to sort out the "keepers" from the throwing rock. It is not intended for the individual who wishes to develop professional, laboratory techniques in gemology.

One of the greatest rewards from tumbling the gem material you collect is in learning to identify more and more of the varieties of gem materials which we may be walking over without recognizing their beauty and value.

Tumbling gem stones requires probably the least outlay of funds of any of the ways of embarking on the rockhound hobby. The dramatic change that can occur in the appearance of rough, weatherbeaten looking rocks when they become polished is a source of constant amazement and pleasure.

Many of the visitors to our beaches of the northwest coast have stopped in our shop and told us they do not know how to identify a rough beach agate, a jasper, or a piece of jade. A similar problem will exist in all of the rock collecting areas, where new members of the rockhound fraternity are wanting to learn how to recognize gem material.

The term "precious stone" and "semi-precious stone" are no longer used by knowledgeable rockhounds. We likewise have an aversion to the practice of some in referring to a "gemmy" gem stone. A stone is either a gem or it is not. It is somewhat like the error of using a double negative.

The principle tests of whether a material can be properly classed as a gem is beauty, hardness or toughness, and to some extent scarcity, although scarcity is only a merchandising factor affecting market value.

Generally, gem stones should have a hardness of about 5½ or more in order to resist the abrasions and wear from normal use.

There are exceptions to this as to any other rule.

Amber, which is a petrified fossil resin, has a hardness of about 2 to 2½. Jet, the black material used in much Indian jewelry by Zuni Indians of the southwest, has a hardness of 2½ to 4. So other factors affecting desirability can offset lack of hardness.

The beauty of a gem stone is a composite of its characteristic color, luster, brilliance, chatoyance, opalescence and asterism.

Luster is the effect of the reflection of light from the surface of a gem, either on a polished surface or a freshly broken face. Following are some examples of the use of these terms.

LUSTER	GEM EXAMPLES
adamantine	diamond
greasy	jade, grossularite garnet
metallic	marcasite
opalescent	chrysoberyl, opal
waxy	turquoise

CHATOYANCY	GEM EXAMPLES
moving beam of light	chrysoberyl (cat's eye)
silky	moonstone, sunstone, star garnet

ASTERISM	GEM EXAMPLES
stars	corundum (ruby, sapphire)
(may be 2, 4, 6 rays)	garnet
	rose quartz
	spinel
	topaz

Field identification of many gem stones may be made when color is used as a test in combination with the test for hardness, specific gravity, fracture and crystal structure.

The study of refraction, dichroism and dispersion of light should be left for those who wish to go more completely into the study of gemology.

The more simple field tests will assist in identifying most of the gem stones apt to be found on collecting trips in this country. There will be cases where the aid of a skilled gemologist will be needed to identify unusual stones.

This is particularly true when gem material may not be in its familiar, or usual shape or color. For instance, grossularite garnet as well as sillimanite may be in a fibrous form or may be crystalline. Also, gem materials may be mixed.

56

We have rough turquoise which also has chrysocolla with it. We have chrysocolla which has malachite in it as well as needles of sagenite. A 1500 lb. rock which we found turned out to be a mixture of grossularite garnet and nephrite jade.

Gemstones, as well as other minerals, do not always follow their "normal" pattern. You should be aware of this possibility and be prepared to study the unusual occurrences. The same gems can vary in hardness, in specific gravity, in color, and in form ... which all adds to the zest of finding and identifying new specimens.

HARDNESS

Hardness reflects durability or wear-ability of a gem stone. Some gems are so outstanding in the other favorable qualities of a gem that relative softness is overlooked. All such gems require re-polishing after considerable wear such as in a ring.

The majority of gems have a hardness of 6½ or more. Moh's scale of hardness runs from #1 (the softest) to #10 (the hardest). Number 10 is more than a thousand percent harder than #I. The scale is not proportionate.

Number 5 is not "half" as hard as #10.

Actually, the difference in hardness between diamond at #10 and emerald at #9, is much more than is the difference in hardness between #9 and #1.

Moh's scale of hardness arranges materials in order of increasing hardness as follows:

Charles S. Hoffman carved this head from jasper.
—Photo by Bert Webber

57

Moh's scale | Material | Test

Moh's scale	Material	Test
# 1	talc	Can be scratched with a finger nail.
# 2	gypsum	Can be scratched with calcite.
# 3	calcite	Can be scratched with a copper coin.
# 4	fluorite	Can be scratched by window glass.
# 5	apatite	Can be scratched with a knife.
# 6	feldspar	Can be scratched with a file.
# 7	quartz	Easily scratches glass. Can be scratched by topaz.
# 8	topaz	Can be scratched by Corundum. Will scratch quartz.
# 9	corundum	Can be scratched by diamond. Will scratch topaz.
#10	diamond	Scratches any other stone. Can be scratched only by another diamond.

Each of the materials listed in the scale will scratch the materials below them in hardness, and in turn can be scratched by all of those materials above them in hardness.

Making scratch tests is not complicated. The thing to be careful about is to avoid a mark caused by **crushing** one stone by another stone. At the other extreme, is to learn to distinguish between a true "scratch" and only a "mark", such as an aluminum nail marks agate. The aluminum mark can be rubbed off. A scrach cannot be rubbed off. This is where a hand lens is extremely helpful.

Hardness and toughness are entirely different characteristics. Jade, which is softer than many other stones, is tougher than most. Diamond, which is the hardest of all minerals, is not as "tough" as jade.

This is why jade has been used for so many thousand years as material to be carved.

If you find or have in your jewelry box a clear stone that you think may be diamond, **do not** hit it with a hammer under the assumption that a diamond will not break. Hitting a diamond ring against the side of the sink while washing dishes can break the diamond.

The erroneous belief was started during the middle ages that if a diamond was placed on an anvil and hit with a hammer, it would "cleave the anvil". Not so! The diamond will break into a thousand pieces.

Think of the large and beautiful diamonds this "test" must have destroyed since that time.

For many of the gem stones of average hardness, other minerals or substances may be used to determine hardness. For the harder gems such as sapphire, ruby, emerald and diamond, a kit of hardness points is advisable. These kits may be purchased at lapidary supply firms.

Specific Gravity

Specific gravity is the weight of any material compared with the weight of an equal volume of water.

A piece of pine may have a specific gravity of 0.5 which means it is only half as heavy as water and will therefore float.

A piece of agate has a specific gravity of 2.6, which means it is 2.6 times heavier than an equal volume of water. The agate therefore sinks in water.

A balance scale can be made in a home workshop, using a ruler as the balance. The formula for determining specific gravity is:

$$\text{Specific Gravity} = \frac{\text{Weight in air}}{\text{Weight in air less weight in water}}$$

In other words, the weight in air is divided by the weight in air less the weight in water. For example, a specimen weighs 12 oz. in air and 9 oz. in water, a loss of 3 oz. when immersed. Applying the formula:

$$\text{Specific Gravity} = \frac{12 \text{ oz.}}{3 \text{ oz.}} \quad \text{or, 4.0 S.G.}$$

A far simpler method, useful not only at home but in the field as well, is the use of "heavy liquids". They are also known as specific gravity fluids.

Three most common of the heavy liquids are SG 2.62, bromoform and xylene; SG 2.89, bromoform; and SG 3.32, methylene iodide. These liquids can be purchased through a rock shop or other lapidary supply house.

There are other specific gravity fluids but the three just mentioned will be found to be the most useful. All of these fluids are strong chemicals and should be handled with care. Keep them away from children.

Use tweezers with all of the heavy liquids for retrieving the specimens. Momentary contact with the skin will not cause harm if quickly washed off. But do not dip your fingers into the bottle. Use tweezers. Keep your hands and the work area clean.

Use a small bottle about 1" in diameter and 3" tall with a tight screw-on lid to hold a small amount of the heavy liquid. When stored, it should be either wrapped or kept in a dark place away from light. Light causes the liquids to deteriorate.

Use the smaller bottle to test the gem fragments. If the stone is to be tested in more than one liquid, it should be washed and dried off before being dropped into a second solution.

The gem stone being tested can be a polished baroque, a finished cab, a faceted stone, or merely a small fragment of rock. In breaking off a small piece of rough gem material, only a pea-sized fragment is necessary. It must be large enough and heavy enough to break thru the surface tension of the heavy liquid.

Drop a small piece of material into one of the liquids and if it floats, poke it down into the liquid with the tweezers. If it is truly lighter than the liquid it will rise to the surface. If it is heavier than the liquid, it will drop to the bottom of the bottle.

If the gem material is about the same specific gravity as the liquid, it will seem to hover somewhere between the surface of the liquid and the bottom of the bottle.

A gem stone that floats in the bottle of bromoform (SG 2.89) has a specific gravity of less than 2.89. A gem stone that sinks in bromoform has a specific gravity of more than 2.89. After using gravity fluids for a while, you will get so you can "heft" the rocks in your hand and come very close to estimating the specific gravity of the material.

Chalcedony or agate has a specific gravity of 2.60 ± .05. This is about average weight for the non-metallic minerals. These are the cryptocrystalline varieties of quartz, with crystals too fine to be seen even with a common microscope. Crystalline quartz, such as the groups of large, terminated crystals sometimes found in geodes, have a specific gravity of 2.66.

The specific gravity of gems may vary slightly due to purity and composition. Weight can be affected, for example, by inclusions of chromite in nephrite jade, plumes of manganese minerals in agate, or additions or loss of water in opal.

There are two gem materials (grossularite garnet and nephrite jade) found on Pacific Coast beaches that are easily confused.

Break off a 1/8" piece and drop it into the bottle of bromoform. If it floats it is neither garnet nor jade. If it sinks, it could be either one. Wash and dry the fragment and drop it into the methylene iodide. If it floats, it could be nephrite jade. If it sinks it is probably grossularite garnet.

These are not absolute tests such as an assay would provide, but will rule out the impossibles from the probables. The final test is, of course, to have the material assayed, or examined under a petrographic microscope. Both grossularite garnet and jade are heavy, tough and have a greasy feel. Both occur quite frequently in shades of green. Without the aid of specific gravity fluids it is frequently difficult to tell them apart. Even then, identification is difficult because of their similar appearance and habit of occurring together in the same rock.

FRACTURE

Gem stones break in characteristic patterns which help in identifying them. Sunstones (a feldspar) break along planes closely related to the crystal structure, making angles of roughly 90°. This type of break is referred to as cleavage.

In the high desert areas of Lake County, Oregon this characteristic cleavage, plus their "honey" color and light weight are sufficient to identify sunstones.

When a gem stone does not break along cleavage or parting planes, it is said to fracture. The majority of gem stones not having natural cleavage, break with either an irregular surface such as crystalline garnet, or will show a conchoidal or shell-like fracture such as obsidian. Crystalline quartz does not show conchoidal fracture. The cryptocrystalline varieties

may show conchoidal fracture, but often show an even to uneven or rough fracture without any indication of a conchoidal fracture.

CRYSTAL SHAPE

Not all gem stones are found in a crystal shape. Some, such as nephrite and jadeite are sometimes botryoidal, but usually massive and found in veins and boulders and do not show a crystal shape. An example of the botryoidal type are the "nuggets" found near Monterey, Calif.

Jade will commonly have hard, smooth "bumps" or "nubbins" sticking up from the rock. These are more common on the waterworn pieces found along the beaches or in the rivers than it is of the jade found in the hills of Wyoming.

Hematite, a black and metallic material, may be in massive veins or boulders such as found in southwestern Oregon and northwestern California associated with jasper. The crystal form may be hexagonal, or more rarely rhombohedral. It can also be reniform. This form seems to be the best quality for use as a gem material.

Some gem materials such as grossularite garnet may occur either in massive form or as cubic crystals. Chrysoprase, bloodstone, lapis lazuli are usually massive or vein material as well as turquoise which is quite often in nodular or nugget form or in veins. Opal may form as pockets in other rock such as mudstone, or as a replacement of wood.

Due to abrasion and breakage during the eons since formation, the original crystal shape may be nearly or even completely lost.

For a complete study of crystallography it is recommended that texts on mineralogy or gemology be studied. For the amateur collector, knowledge of a few principle crystal types will aid in recognizing a large percentage of the gem stones. The following summary of characteristics of gem materials does not include all gems. Instead, major examples are shown of the gems falling into each crystal system, together with notes on color, hardness, specific gravity, fracture, and usual type of occurrence.

In addition to the gem examples listed under the crystal systems in the table, there are other materials used as gems which cannot be classified this way.

Amber, an amorphous fossil resin, is sometimes found on Pacific Coast beaches. With a specific gravity of 2.0 to 2.5 it is light enough to be washed ashore.

Amber can be distinguished from some of its substitutes such as glass and bakelite (or plastic) by immersing it in a saturated solution of salt.

Characteristics Of Major Gem Materials

CRYSTAL SYSTEM: ISOMETRIC

Gem	Color	Hardness	Sp. Gr.	Fracture	Occurrence
Diamond	clr, y, blu	10	3.5	cleavage	crystal
Garnet	rd, y, gr, etc.	6½ - 7½	3.5 - 4.3	irregular	crystal
Grossularite	gr, y, wh	6½	3.5	irregular	cubic; massive
Lazurite	azure blue	5 - 5½	2.4	cleavage	massive
Spinel	rd, wh, blue	8	3.5 - 4.1		crystal

CRYSTAL SYSTEM: HEXAGONAL

Gem	Color	Hardness	Sp. Gr.	Fracture	Occurrence
Apatite	clr, br, gr, blu	5	3.2		crystal, massive
Benitoite	blue	6½	3.7		crystal
Beryl					
Aquamarine	gr-blue	7½ - 8	2.72 ± .05	basal cl	hex xl, v. stria.
Emerald	green	7½ - 8	2.72 ± .05	basal cl	hex xl, v. stria.
Golden Beryl	golden-y	7½ - 8	2.72 ± .05	basal cl	hex xl, v. stria.
Morganite	pink to rose	7½ - 8	2.72 ± .05	basal cl	hex xl, v. stria.
Chrysoberyl	gr, br, rd, y	8½	3.7 - 3.8		twin crystals
Corundum					
Ruby	red	9	4.0	cubic	crystal
Sapphire	wh, blue	9	4.0	cubic	crystal

Gem	Color	Hardness	Sp. Gr.	Fracture	Occurrence
Hematite	black	6½	4.9 - 5.2	irregular	ms; reniform
Quartz					
Crystalline					
Amethyst	pur, violet	7	2.66	irregular	hex xl hor stria.
Citrine	yellowish	7	2.66	irregular	hex xl hor stria.
Rock Crystal	colorless	7	2.66	irregular	hex xl hor stria.
Rose Quartz	rose	7	2.66	irregular	ms; xls rare
Smokey Quartz	y-br	7	2.66	irregular	ms; xl hor stria
Cryptocrystalline					
Agate	various	7	2.60 ± .05	conch; irr	ms; veins, nod, etc.
Bloodstone	gr w/red dots	7	2.60 ± .05	conch; irr	ms; veins
Chert	lighter colors	7	2.60 ± .05	conch; irr	ms; nod
Flint	darker colors	7	2.60 ± .05	conch; irr	ms; nod
Jasper	various	7	2.60 ± .05	conch; irr	ms; nod
Prase	green	7	2.60 ± .05	conch; irr	ms
Tourmaline	rd, pk, y, blu, gr	7 - 7½	3.0 - 3.25		xl w/vert stria

CRYSTAL SYSTEM: TETRAGONAL

Gem	Color	Hardness	Sp. Gr.	Fracture	Occurrence
Vesuvianite	gr, blu, rd, y, br	6½	3.4	irregular	xls; ms
Zircon	clr, gr, rd, gray	6½ - 7½	4.65 - 4.70		xls

CRYSTAL SYSTEM: ORTHORHOMBIC

Gem	Color	Hardness	Sp. Gr.	Fracture	Occurrence
Peridot	olive-gr, br	6½ - 7	3.3 - 3.4	irregular	xl
Sillimanite	br, gr, wh	6 - 7	3.2	basal clv	commonly ms
Topaz	clr, y, pk, blu, gr	8	3.4 - 3.6	irregular	xl
Variscite	gr	3½ - 4½	2.6	irregular	ms; or nod

CRYSTAL SYSTEM: MONOCLIC

Gem	Color	Hardness	Sp. Gr.	Fracture	Occurrence
Azurite	blue	3½ - 4	3.8	1 perf. cl	xls; or ms
Epidote	gr, y, bl	6 - 7	3.4 - 3.5		xl
Jade					
Jadeite	gr, y, wh, pur, etc.	6½ - 7	3.3 - 3.5	irregular	ms
Nephrite	gr, wh, gray, etc.	6½	2.95 - 3.0	irregular	ms; botry boulders
Malachite	green	3½ - 4	3.9 - 4.0	irregular	ms; tufts; rosette
Moonstone	clr, blue-wh	6	2.6	-90° cl	xl (some tricl)

CRYSTAL SYSTEM: TRICLINIC

Gem	Color	Hardness	Sp. Gr.	Fracture	Occurrence
Rhodonite	pk, rd, w/blu veins	5½ - 6	3.6 - 3.7	rt. angle	xl; or ms
Sunstone	honey-color	6	2.6 - 2.7	irr.	xl
Turquoise	blue, green	6 - 6½	2.6 - 2.8		ms, nod, vein

Abbrev.:

cl	cleavage	nod	nodules	blu	blue	pk	pink
con	conchoidal	stria	striations	br	brown	pur	purple
irr	irregular	xl	crystal	clr	clear	wh	white
ms	massive	bl	black	gr	green	y	yellow

65

Amber will float in it. The glass, bakelite and plastic will sink. Amber will also generate static electricity when rubbed briskly on wool or nylon, while some of the substitutes will not.

Opal is an amorphous silicate frequently found with agate. It has a conchoidal fracture, has a hardness of about 6 to 6½ and a specific gravity of 2.2. It can be transluscent or opaque and occurs in many colors. The type with "fire" in it is used for gems. Even without "fire", jelly opal of good color makes beautiful gems.

Opal is found filling cavities in igneous rock, in thunder eggs, petrified wood and frequently in layers with agate in agate nodules. In some of the desert areas, opal is found in small cavities in a consolidated form of mud or clay.

Opal can be distinguished from agate by its lighter weight, lesser hardness and its "waxy" or vitreous luster.

Chrysocolla is an amorphous gem found associated with other copper minerals such as turquoise. Chrysocolla is referred to as "silica" by the miners who find most of it.

The best grade of chrysocolla is a fine transluscent color known as "electra blue", has a hardness of 7 and a specific gravity of 2.0 to 2.4. Softer varieties are less adaptable to hand working and may be satisfactorily tumbled for use in baroque jewelry.

It is possible to find these gem materials mentioned in this section within the United States. Naturally, some are found in abundance in certain areas while others are quite scarce. But the possibility always exists of finding beautiful gem material.

The individual who has learned some of the ways of identifying various gem stones will have a far better chance of recognizing material worth picking up. Without such knowledge, we can each walk over a small fortune and not recognize it.

State geologists in the Department of Mineral Industries in Oregon have told us that in all probability most diamonds found on the beaches or in placer gravels of this state have been discarded under the assumption they were worthless. They can look a lot like a piece of glass.

There is material available on the beach to use in checking a specimen. Find a piece of agate or jasper with a rough edge, or break a piece to obtain a sharp edge. If the agate or jasper will scratch the specimen, it is probably glass, a fragment of a bottle or of a Japanese fish float that washed ashore and broke. If the specimen will scratch the agate or the jasper, then hold on to it, for it could be a diamond. Further tests would be warranted.

During a visit to the gem section of the Smithsonian Museum in Washington, D.C. we saw on display a brilliant yellow diamond of a carat and a quarter. It was found on the beach in Curry County, Oregon near Bandon.

The gem materials that are currently being found on the beaches in this area of southwestern Oregon include:

AGATE:
  Clear
  Banded
  Blue
  Carnelian
  Dendritic
  Moonstone agate
  Moss agate
  Rainbow (Iris)
  Sagenite
  Sand agates
  Water agates (enhydros)
  Fortification agate
BLOODSTONE
GROSSULARITE GARNET
JADE (nephrite)
JASPER
PETRIFIED FOSSILS (clams, dinny bone, etc.)
PETRIFIED MYRTLEWOOD
RHODONITE

There are some common garden-variety of tests which help identify these materials when we go rock hunting or beachcombing. They also help in filling the rock sack, but always leave some for the next fellow. Specialize in variety and quality, not quantity.

Don't walk a sandy beach with your head down, hunting for agate on the sand. Instead, look around for a gravel bed. If the waves are washing across it, then stay there a while and keep watching the gravel as it is moved by the water.

In walking back and forth across the gravel, look toward the sunlight. Agates can be spotted this way at a considerable distance, for light will show through many of them.

When you pick up a rock and wonder if it is an agate, check to see if it is transluscent. Most agates are, but not all of them are. Look for the small, tell-tale triangles that are common to agate.

Agate usually has a few shiny surfaces. The more shine a rock has, the harder it is. The harder it is, the better polish it will take.

If you let a rock dry and it looks sugary, it is probably sugar quartz and not an agate. It will not take a bright polish.

Another characteristic of beach agate is the white covering or coating on many of them. Most of this comes off during tumbling. If you wish to retain the white patterns, then give the agate less rough grinding.

Check for water agates by holding them toward the light and rolling them around between the fingers and watch for any movement of light spot or shadow inside the agate. Sometimes the water bubbles can be seen this way in rough agates, but most water agates are found after the agates have been tumbled.

Some of the large blue agates look almost like a piece of black basalt. Many times the only test is to saw them. If you see the small indentation on one that shows the small triangle pattern, then it is most likely an agate. These "blues" are quite dark, almost a blue-black in color and make beautiful jewelry.

Sawing is also the test for rainbow or iris agate. When you find an agate with fine banding or fortification it should be cut across the banding if you wish to check it for iris. Make the slices very thin. When viewed toward the light, a slice of iris agate will show a rainbow-like flash of colors. Immersion in kerosene oil before viewing this type of agate aids in bringing out the play of colors.

Sagenite agate may have a layer of small holes or depressions on one side, about the size of pencil dots. In small stones, the sagenite will show up when the agate is tumbled. The term "sagenite" refers to "needles" in the agate caused by various minerals. The word is pronounced with a short "a", and the accent on the "g", with the "g" pronounced as though it were a "j".

In looking for bloodstone pick up the green jasper and see if any of it has red dots or red markings. Well marked specimens may be found in the beach gravels.

The grossularite garnet is mostly opaque white or an ice-like transluscent stone. Not all of it takes a good polish. The best stones are the pink ones. The green and the yellowish ones look a lot like nephrite. Avoid the ones with numerous black areas in them.

In searching for jade on the beach, glance ahead at least twenty-five feet, looking for any stones that appear wet even though they may be dry. When you find one that looks wet, pick it up and rub it. If it is jade it will be heavy and have a distinctly "greasy" feel. It will also be bumpy and worn unevenly. When clinked against another rock it has almost an iron-like ring to it. It will be nearly impossible to break with a rock hammer.

Jade found on the beach is usually smooth on the surface and not like the jade found in the hills of Wyoming, which has a rough, reddish-brown rind on it.

The petrified fossils look just like what they are, except for the small pieces of dinny bone. Much of it is classified in error as being petrified whalebone, probably because it is found near the ocean. Look for the small, cell-like structures which identify it as petrified bone. The degree of replacement by agate will vary. The best polish will show on the more agatized pieces.

The rhodonite in the beach gravel is extremely hard for this material. It is not an easy stone to recognize. Look for the rose-pink color and the black lines or veins.

In the streams or in the hills, the rhodonite will usually be black. This is the result of oxidation of the manganese minerals. It will be necessary to chip off a small section with a rock hammer. If it is rhodonite, the pink color will be shown under the black, oxidized surface.

The petrified myrtlewood is found along the beaches of Coos and Curry counties in southwestern Oregon. The pieces almost have to be picked up and examined in order to be recognized. Look for the characteristic grain as shown in the natural wood.

The best colors of the myrtlewood are brown and deep red. Leave the black ones. Very few pieces of the black will polish. Some of the black can be bleached out by soaking the material in a solution of chlorox.

The black is probably due to minerals in the soil, which have permeated the wood. Whether this was done before or after the wood became petrified, we do not know. We do not agree with the theory that the wood became "carbonized". That theory was ruled out when a rockhound friend of ours who is a timber faller, cut a myrtle tree that was about half and half black and natural color. This was a growing tree.

The people who process the natural myrtlewood for bowls, trays and other beautiful objects say that the attractive patterns in the wood are caused by minerals in the soil where the trees grow. The more mineral, the more colors in the wood.

This petrified myrtlewood is estimated by geologists to be approximately 100 million years old. Myrtlewood (California laurel) is unique to a small area touching the south Oregon coast but is also found as far south as Los Angeles, as well as inland from east of Sacramento to near Yosemite National Park.

No description of beach materials would be complete without reference to "moonstones". The term has been used for many years and refers to the small, rounded water-clear agates which have an opalescent, bluish appearance.

The opalescence in the agate is caused by the "planes" in which the agate has formed. These planes are known as "turtle-back" because of their design. The pattern is much more apparent in a slice of clear, turtle-back agate than it is in the uncut stone. These agates are found on many Oregon beaches and are the same type as those found on southern California beaches.

These are not moonstones but are agate. A moonstone is a feldspar. An agate is a silicate. Relatively soft stones such as a moonstone would quickly wear away in beach gravel and disappear.

So when the term "moonstone" or "moonstone agate" is applied to this beach material, keep in mind that it is really agate ... a gem in its own right.

"Old Man of the Mountain." These are pieces of jade sawed from a bigger piece. Not retouched
—Photo by Bert Webber

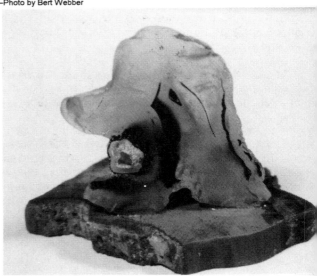

9. Tips on Hunting for Gem Material

The best place to hunt gem material as a starter is right in your own locality. You may be surprised at the possibilities.

Investigate all of the areas where movement of water could have sorted, or scattered or collected gravel and rocks. Look along the shores of beaches, lake shores, borders of rivers, streams, and even in dry washes. Check areas where wind erosion might have uncovered gravel by blowing sand away from the larger rock.

Older deposits of gravel should also be checked. Stream beds were not always at their present levels. Look for stretches of gravel in road cuts and land-slide areas.

Most of the continental United States was covered at one or more times by ancient seas. Gravels and minerals were deposited or accumulated during these periods. Look for beds of conglomerate, which may appear to be like rough concrete. The sand and gravel will be "cemented" together by heat, pressure, and mineral solutions. Gem materials may be included in such gravels.

There are other sedimentary formations deposited by water action that can hold gem materials. These include sandstone, limestone, shale, mudstone and chalk. The "white cliffs of Dover" are chalk cliffs which have in them pieces of flint, used in manufacture of beautiful artifacts by prehistoric men.

Many times these former ocean beds can be spotted by the presence of fossil shells. If these shells are agatized they make attractive specimens and beautiful jewelry. A common name for one type is "turritella" agate, which is a misnomer inasmuch as the proper name is oxytrema octracods. These agatized fossil shells are found on Pacific beaches and also in the mountains of Utah and Colorado, at the sites of former ocean beds.

The Rocky Mountains were pushed up from the bottom of the sea, as were the mountains of the Coast Range along the Pacific Coast.

Another type of deposit of gravel containing gem materials are glacial moraines. These vast moving rivers of ice pushed up large deposits of gravel and other debris at the edges of the glacier and in front.

Evidence of glacial action are found in many of our states. It is believed by many of the experts, that the diamonds found in the states adjoining the Great Lakes were deposited there by glacial action. This is also true of agate beds in the gravel of mid-western states such as Iowa and South Dakota.

A study of rock-types will aid in finding gem materials. Agate may form in many types of rock, from sandstone (a sedimentary rock) to lava (a volcanic rock).

Agate is a silicate and much of the agate is found in rock high in silica, such as rhyolite. This is the rock in eastern Oregon in which the plume agate is found, as well as the thunder eggs.

Rhyolite is sometimes greenish in color and sometimes reddish. It may be soft and crumbly where it is undergoing severe erosion or it may be exceedingly hard and require a star drill and a hammer to dig out any agate. These rhyolite cliffs can be spotted by the streaks of white silica which mark the rock.

Along the Pacific Coast counties we have found agate in rhyolite, sandstone and black lava as well as in nearly all of the sedimentary types of formations mentioned previously.

Petrified wood can be found in many of the gravel beds in agate areas. This material may have been formed by a replacement process in which the wood is replaced by silica, in which case it is referred to as being "petrified wood". If the replacement was by agate, then the wood is known as "agatized wood". If it is replaced by opal, it is known as "opalized wood".

Because the original form of the wood is preserved, it is also correctly referred to as a fossil.

All of these types of wood may have been moved by water and collected in gravel deposits. But the search for wood should also include the areas where the wood was formed.

The wood may have been covered by pumice or lava while on a lake shore. The wood in such cases may have moved downhill from its original location. A good procedure is to look for "float" in the creek beds and washes. When pieces of petrified wood are found, keep moving uphill to locate the area from which the wood is being carried.

Gem materials such as garnet may also be found in the gravels of creek beds. By prospecting upstream, the source of the garnet may be found in ledges of mica schist in which the garnets were formed.

Quartz crystals may have formed in the "vugs" or openings in quartz veins, or may come from geodes. Amethyst, citrine, and smoky quartz (which are all colored quartz crystals) may have been similarly formed. Sometimes they are even found in large hollow sections of petrified logs.

Gem materials such as rhodonite and rhodochrosite should be searched for in areas of "basic" rocks where traces of manganese are found.

In localities having copper, there is a possibility of finding turquoise, malachite, and chrysocolla.

In areas having chromite or hematite (usually found in the same general area), search for chrome garnet as well as gem hematite (the botryoidal form).

The serpentine areas of the Pacific coast, as well as the inland areas having serpentine, such as Wyoming, should be searched for jade and for grossularite garnet. Both of these gem materials are formed in serpentine as a metamorphic rock.

A study of the rock types in which gem materials are formed, as well as study of the sedimentary formation in which the gem material may have accumulated, will aid in the search for gem stones.

The beaches are fruitful places to hunt because every tide moves new gravel. Every day you may look over gravel accumulations that no one else has seen.

Aside from the petrified myrtlewood, which is found on the beaches only in southwestern Oregon, the other gem materials listed previously are found on most beaches of the west. This assumes the presence of hard gravels, with which the gem materials are associated.

These gravels move, and disappear or re-appear from one tide to the next. The best time to hunt the beaches is in the winter when the rough surf washes away the sand and washes in new beds of gravel.

If you hunt on the beaches during summer, be on the beach during low tide, especially during any "minus" tides when the tide goes farther out and more rock and gravel is exposed.

The best time for hunting many of the inland regions for gem material is in the summer, for some of the higher elevations like the high desert of eastern Oregon may have snow on it in winter. However, other desert areas will be dangerously hot and arid during summer and should be hunted in spring or fall.

The best time to hunt river agate such as Montana agate in the Yellowstone River areas is in the spring before the warmer weather melts the snow pack and raises the water level. Much of this hunting is done from boats, checking the gravel bars in the middle of the river.

High water in the rivers can be a problem. It helps uncover new gravel but can restrict hunting when the water level is too high. We have been at the Fraser River in British Columbia in June to look for jade when the river was out of its banks and all of the gravel was under water.

Local rockhounds advise making the trip to the Fraser River within the period from December through February when the water level is low. The government has restricted the filing of any new mining claims on the best jade area of the river, so as to keep it open for rockhounds. The opportunity of finding jade on the Fraser has been greatly improved for the amateur collector.

Gem hunting maps and guides are published and are on sale at most rock shops, covering the major collecting areas.

The Bureau of Land Management administers part of the federal lands and part is administered by the U.S. Forest Service. Both agencies publish excellent maps which are a real aid in rock hunting.

In the western states, approximately half the area is federally owned lands. Most of these lands are open to rock hunting if other property and property rights (such as grazing) are protected.

The 400 mile coast-line in Oregon is public property and open to rock hounds except for a few miles of beach owned under "Spanish Land Grants". You may hunt on the public beaches, but must use public access and not cross private property in getting to or from the beach.

A good procedure is to decide where you want to hunt, then write to a chamber of commerce or to someone else in that area and ask about the best times to collect. But don't overlook the published maps and guides. They can save you many tanks of gas in looking for those good spots for gem materials.

Then review the methods of identifying gem stones.

Your trips will be much more rewarding and will provide opportunities of adding to the quality and variety of your collection, with many choice items for your tumbler.

10. How To Pan Gold

Because gold is heavier than most sediments and gravels in a stream, it and other heavy metals called "black sand" (including pyrite, magnetite, ilmenite, chromite, garnet), can be collected in a gold pan when the correct panning techniques are used.

For the most part, vessels for use in gold panning and the methods of panning are unchanged over the years. The beveled sided dishpan is the traditional utensil for panning for gold. But anything that will hold water, and of course, the dirt and gravel from a likely spot, will do. However, if one expects good results from the effort of getting to a site, then spending the time bending over and wading in cold water, the use of a proper pan is really essential.

There is nothing sophisticated about panning for gold. Just about anyone can to it. The technique, possibly overly simplified, is merely placing dirt believed to contain gold, and water, in a pan then shaking it until the gold, which is heavier than water and most sediment, sinks to the bottom of the pan. Then pick out the gold.

Some "miners" who go out on a weekend looking strictly for gold as a small business, may carry a metal detector. This is a short cut to locating more likely sites than just guesswork.

The "riffle" pan, is far better than the old fashioned straight pan. This pan has ridges along one side that trap gold as one pours off sediments and water.

Another supplemental "pan" is really a screen with a frame around it. Its purpose is to separate large and small gravel. Holes in the screen should be no less than about 1/4-inch or larger than 3/4 to 1-inch. The screen appears to work best with dry matter as wet material tends to clog the holes. After basic shaking (sifting), the larger pieces can be inspected with a magnifying glass for gold particles. The smaller parts, that fell through the holes, maybe directly into the gold pan, are mixed with water then shaken in the usual manner.

All the glitters is not gold

Pyrite, commonly called "fool's gold," has tricked many a professional as well as weekend-fun gold seeker since the beginning of placer mining.

On close examination, pyrite does not really look like gold. Pyrite has a brassy color and is sometimes tarnished. Because it occurs in crystals, it changes shade as one holds a specimen hand and rotates it in the sun. Gold, on the other hand, is always gold colored. It is soft and can be bent (malleable).

When you see gold colored flecks that either float on the top of the water or are so light weight they easily wash over the edge of the pan, you probably have small pieces or "books: of mica. Mica is a transparent and heat resistant material that has been used in doors of wood stoves to see the condition of the fire inside. Mica was extensively used as the insulator for the element in toasters. Mica breaks fairly easily into flat, thin sheets.

Because Mica comes in a variety of colors, the goldish color is sometimes misidentified as gold by inexperienced panners.

When you are lucky with panning and discover gold in your pan, it may be in any number of shapes. These can be mere flakes, wire-like pieces, feather-shaped crystals, lumps or nuggets. These pieces of gold vary in size from microscopic to as large as a fist.

Great stories have been told of how large the nuggets were, and indeed, there are many large nuggets in museums on exhibit. In Oregon, the very famous Armstrong nugget (80.4 oz.) is seen in the display in the U.S. National Bank in Baker City, Oregon. Baker City is in the heart of eastern Oregon's gold country and is easily accessible from Interstate-84 in the northeast section of Oregon. (See chapter on Museums)

Gold panners are always optimistic. Like Winston Churchill, they "never give up."

Weekend-gold seekers who want to pan for gold, need be aware of hundreds of staked claims throughout Oregon. But there are "open" areas in Oregon for public panning.

All areas of "State Lands" below the vegetation line on navigable rivers and streams, as well as ocean beaches, belong to the State of Oregon. These are open for recreational gold panning.

. In addition, panning is permitted on almost all streams and rivers in campgrounds on BLM and U. S. Forest Service land.

Specific Locations In Oregon

From time-to-time, federal and state laws and regulation change. Always check with proper authority *first*. Accept the content of this book for gold panning locations as "guidelines" only.

(1) Quartzville Recreational Corridor in the Western Cascades of the Salem BLM District. Obtain specific information at the BLM office in Salem.

(2) Butte Falls Recreational Area about 45 miles northeast of Medford. Obtain specific information from the BLM office in Medford.

(3) Applegate Ranger District about 25 miles southwest of Medford. Obtain specific information from the U.S. Forest Service office in Medford.

(4) There are three areas set aside for gold panning in the Wallowa-Whitman National Forest in northeast Oregon. Obtain specific information from the U.S. Forest Service in Baker City.

Additional gold panning areas:

•The Eagle Forks Campground, northwest of Richmond in Pine Ranger District at Halfway.

•McCully Forks Campground west of Sumpter, Baker Ranger District

•Deer Creek campground north of Phillips Lake, Baker Ranger District

•Powder River Recreational Area, just below Mason Dam, Baker Ranger District.

• If one is unsure about the status of the land, investigate with the nearest appropriate State, BLM or U.S. Forest Service offices.

It is wise to get permission before setting foot on private land – even to cross private land between two known public land areas.

OREGON LEAVERITE

If what you might find along the way is obviously of historical or scientific value, do not disturb it:
LEAVE ER RIGHT where you found it !
It is the "Oregon" way. It is the law.

Equipment needed for gold panning:

Gold pan
Garden hand trowel
Tweezers
Small Magnet
Magnifying glass
Small container (transparent pill bottle
    with screw or snap top; plastic 35mm
    film canister with snap top)
Hand towel

Ribbed gold pan (top) is more efficient for retaining gold in the pan rather than gold accidentally washing over the edge as happened for a hundred years in the "old standard" **(lower)** pan. –Gold and pans courtesy of Oregon Trail Mercantile, Baker City.
—Bert Webber photos

Armstrong nugget at 80.4 ounces, is exhibited in U.S. National Bank Baker City.

1. After digging in the bottom of a shallow creek, below the easily seen loose gravel and preferably to bed rock (the most likely area to find gold, on the downstream side of large boulders), fill, but do not over-fill a gold pan. Take care with the trowel or shovel due to risk of losing flecks of gold while lifting the tool out of the water. Try not to let water and sediments dribble off the tool for doing so allows any gold to drain right back into the creek. Place between about half to two-thirds full of soil and gravel from the stream bank or channel.

Prospector of the 1920's sits down on the job. His tub is filled with water, a pile of gold-bearing ore near his feet. Many of today's gold-seeking rockhounds take to the field and bring back a load of ore to be worked at home in their spare time.

Top Layer of Gravel is Washed Away

2. Experience indicates that the better sites are away from swiftly running water. Place the pan totally under water to break up lumps of clay, then discard the stones. Better to set the stones aside for later inspection with a magnifying glass in one's search for gold.

3. Holding the pan under the water's surface with your hands on opposite sides of the pan. Use hands to break up stubborn clay lumps then rotate, vigorously, the pan halfway back and forth rapidly agitating to wash out the dirt (clay). The shaking and rotating motions should be in all directions. Do not be gentle. This swirls the water and causes heavy matter to sink to the bottom of the pan. Take your time.

4. Continue holding the pan under the surface of the water but tilt the pan forward away from your body and slightly downward. Continue to rotate and shake the pan to let the light gravel and sand dribble out the front. Push top matter and large chunks of rock out of the pan with your thumbs. Don't rush. Sloppy draining of the pan, with unbroken lumps of clay going over the edge, may return much gold back into the creek. Better, always slurry your pan's drool into a bucket so the content can be re-washed. Don't hurry. "Haste makes waste" – you lose your gold.

5. Take the pan with the residue, probably now reduced to about 4 cupfuls of concentrated sediments, along with some water out of the stream. Rotate the pan in a circular motion but watch carefully what is happening: The water is separating lighter from heavier materials and the gold, if gold is present and you are working your pan correctly, is lagging behind other material in the bottom of the pan. Don't rush!

—Numbered gold panning pictures courtesy of Oregon
Department of Geology and Mineral Industries

6. Stop rotating the pan. If you are fortunate, you will see a few flecks of
gold in the dark material in the bottom of the pan. Carefully pour out
the water and let the black sand and the gold dry. (It may be good to
place the damp black sand with the gold, in a closed-top bucket to
be taken home and finished there.) When dry, lift out most of the
black sand with a small magnet, then separate the gold from the
remainder of the sediments with tweezers. There may be more than
gold in your pan! Be alert for silver.

**Jim Picket, Sr., and his family, pan gold in Canyon Creek, Grant
County in 1934.** (—Photo courtesy of Grant County Museum, Canyon City) **In
the decade of the Great Depression, thousands of people living in
rural areas on land that historically had been rich in gold, spent
every minute they could prospecting for gold.**

**Many were unlucky. But many
fed their families on backyard
mining. A few did very well. An
exciting account of this is in
*Jacksonville, Oregon; Antique
Town in a Modern Age* (see
bibliography).**

Gold Flakes Collect at Edge of Sand

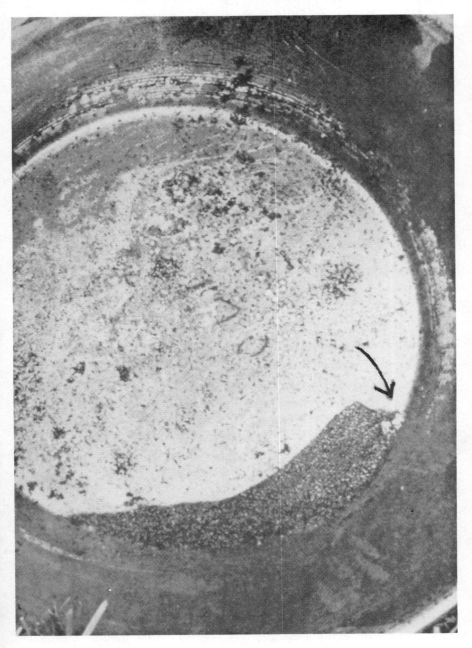

(TOP) Beach sand from northern Curry County traditionally contains gold. Bucket of sand is exhibited at Curry County Historical Society, Gold Beach. (LOWER) A "pinch-of-gold" was standard for trade before coins became common and was worth about $1 in trade. A pinch was the amount of dust a miner could hold between a thumb and forefinger. Merchants were careful to see that fingers were thoroughly dry before pinching. At variance also was the size of a man's fingers.

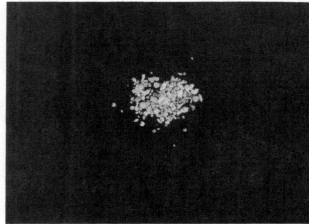

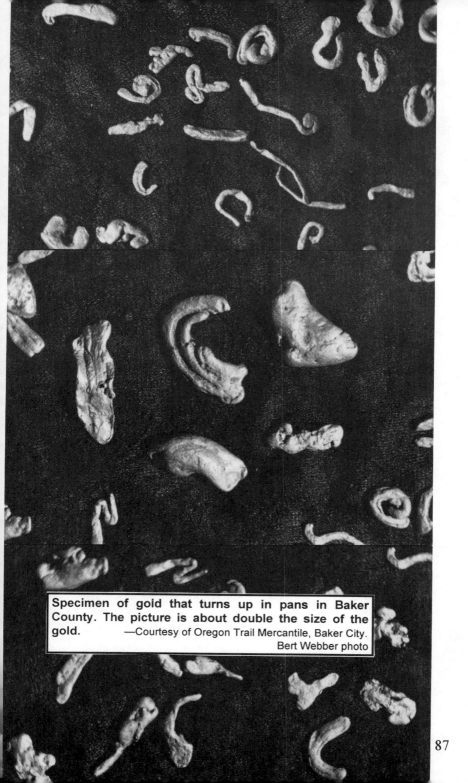

Specimen of gold that turns up in pans in Baker County. The picture is about double the size of the gold. —Courtesy of Oregon Trail Mercantile, Baker City.
Bert Webber photo

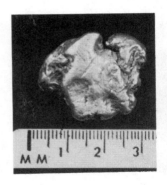 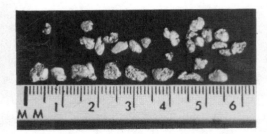

(TOP AND LOWER) **Nuggets are displayed alongside rulers to indicate size of the nuggets.** (CENTER) **nugget jewelry.**
—Courtesy of Rogue Valley Coin and Jewelry Exchange - Medford.
Bert Webber photos

Take Time to Sample Gravel from Ancient Stream Beds. There May be Gold!

There is a great tendency among some rockhounders to throw caution to the wind and let one's sense of wonder steer a car off the highway and onto a set of tire ruts that may or may not go anywhere. Old prospectors did this with their mules. Modernsters do it with their cars. Jeep trails in the Central Oregon desert are often very dusty but sometimes lead to great acerages ideal for hunting rocks – see the map and list on pages vi and vii. To drive a "city" car in heavy dust can be risky. Dust penetrates everywhere including into the engine compartment. When a car stalls due to dust, one may have a long walk for help, then must face the cost of hiring a tow truck. Personal risk is great for motorists who do not carry drinking water, wear good shoes and have a hat. Carry a cellular telephone but realize it may not work in far-flung places.

Oregon Trail Regional Museum, at the corner of Grove and Campbell Streets, Baker City, hosts permanent exhibits of minerals, crystals, semiprecious stones and gems.

—Bert Webber photo

Museums
Some Outstanding "Rock" Exhibits

In Oregon, the very famous Armstrong nugget (80.4 oz.) is seen as part of a display in the U.S. National Bank in Baker City, Oregon. Baker City is in the heart of eastern Oregon's gold country and is easily accessible from Interstate-84 in the northeast section of Oregon. The exhibit is on the floor of the main banking room and is open during banking ours.

The Baker County Historical Society maintains a very large public museum, named The Oregon Trail Regional Museum, on Campbell Street at Grove Street in Baker City. It holds the famous Cavin-Warfell Collection of minerals, crystals, semiprecious stones and gems.

This collection was put together by the Cavin sisters who were born in Baker City and spent most of their lives there. Experts claim this assortment compares favorably with the most outstanding collections of its type in the United States.

The museum's Wyatt Collection includes more than 2,000 agate and jasper *cabochons* mounted on 113 glass plates. These are exhibited in specially designed cases for easy viewing. Most of these examples are called "picture" agates. In addition, the Wyatt superb collection of polished Fire Obsidian is also in the museum. Wyatt was a native of Baker City. Although he moved to Central Oregon later in life, his collection was returned to his home town for permanent exhibit.

In Western Oregon is the Crater Rock Museum at Central Point. This city is on Interstate-5, about 4 miles north of Medford. The museum is at 2002 Scenic Avenue east of Highway 99 and is easiest accessed from the freeway at Exit 35.

The Crater Rock Museum is owned and operated by the Roxy Ann Gem and Mineral Society, Inc., a non-profit organization. The museum exhibits one of the finest collections on the west coast including a collection of uncut amethyst in cathedral formations. It is noted for its unique exhibit of polished petrified woods, its prominent and unique collection of early American Indian artifacts which includes the Traevell Turpin display of Indian effigies, small fired clay figures. One series depicts the art of flintknapping, the process used to produce stone-age tools.

The Henan Dinosaur Eggs

Undoubtedly the most particular exhibit at Crater Rock Museum is the nest of several Ornithischian dinosaur eggs. From the Henan Province of China, these eggs were a gift to the museum where they are on permanent display. Only fifty eggs were allowed outside China. These went primarily to scientific research centers. Crater Rock Museum is the only museum in the United States known to have Henan dinosaur eggs on continuous public exhibit. These eggs are estimated to be 100 million years old.

The Crater Rock Museum and Gift Shop has been a favorite point of interest to traveling rockhounds since it opened in 1954 with specimens originally collected by Delmer and Freida Smith.

The fossil collection of vertebrate and invertebrate fossils date to the Cambrian, some 500 million years ago. Ever seen a 250 million year old petrified pine cone with intact seeds? One is here.

Bibliography

Evans, James R. *Flagstaff Hill on the National Historic Oregon Trail; An Interpretative Guide.* Webb Research Group. 1992.

Hoffman, Charles S. *The Search For Oregon's Lost Blue Bucket Mine; The Stephen Meek Wagon Train of 1845 – An Oregon Documentary.* Webb Research Group. 1992.

Lagal, Roy. *The New Gold Panning is Easy.* Ram. 1992.

Pearl, Richard M. *How to Know the Minerals and Rocks.* Signet. 1955.

_____. *Successful Mineral Collecting and Prospecting.* Signet. 1954.

Webber, Bert, *Dredging For Gold; Documentary.* Webb Research Group. 1994.

_____. *Gold Mining in Oregon.* Webb Research Group. 1995

Webber, Bert and Margie. *Jacksonville, Oregon; Antique Town in a Modern Age.* Webb Research Group. 1994.

Arsenic in Agate found near Dexter, Oregon
—Photo by Bert Webber

Charles S. Hoffman
1907-1992

About the Author

Charles S. Hoffman acquired a Master Degree in Sociology from Oregon State University he then accepted a Teaching Assistant position in Sociology at Stanford University. While at Stanford, Hoffman continued graduate study into the migration of Chinese to the west coast of the United States. Hoffman was a "researcher's researcher" for he literally left no stones unturned (pun intended) in his quest for information. In his study concerning the 1845 wagon route along which is the lost blue bucket mine, he spent much time at the Library of Congress in Washington D. C., then took to the field spending three summers in the isolated and dangerous Central Oregon desert. With painstaking labor, he located the trail and documented his findings in his book, *The Search For Oregon's Lost Blue Bucket Mine* (see bibliography).

Mr. Hoffman was always amazed with Mother Earth and what it is made of. He related, "There are rocks, rocks, rocks, and sand — ground up rocks"! He was a serious "rockhounder" for years. He learned everything about rocks he could digest, then learned how to polish them. Hoffman often built his own rock-finishing equipment. He owned and operated jewelry making shops in Arizona and on the south Oregon coast and in Central Oregon at Bend.

The first edition of his rockhound book was privately printed on

Hoffman's off-road outfit of early 1970's used for exploring Central Oregon desert for 1845 wagon route along which is the lost blue bucket mine.

the Oregon coast in 1970, then revised and expanded in 1973. He sold all rights to his book to Bert Webber, publisher at Webb Research Group Publishers, in 1991. In that year, Webber added some pictures to the book as well as an Index. During the summer of 1992, Mr. Hoffman, at age 85, in Bend, Oregon, passed away.

Bert Webber is a Research Photojournalist and publisher. He holds a degree in journalism from Whitworth College, and the Master of Library Science degree after graduate studies at Portland State University and University of Portland.

Webber, wishing to continue to recognize Charles Hoffman's expertise about rocks and the polishing of them, and the making of jewelry with them, had told Hoffman that subsequent editions of his book would continue to bear his name.

The book was further expanded in 1993 by the addition of more photographs and a section readers requested, the "Personal Notes" pages in the back of the book.

Due to an increased public interest about gold panning, that section of the book was expanded with special illustrations on each step in the process for the 1997 edition. In addition, the section on museums, titled, "Some Outstanding 'Rock' Exhibits" is also added as is a bibliography. The earlier index has been expanded to include the additions to this book. <>

Rockhound country along Oregon Highway 26 not far from John Day Fossil Beds National Monument. —Bert Webber photo.

Index

Page numbers in *Italic bold* type are illustrations

Personal Notes

Personal Notes

Personal Notes

Personal Notes